BEETLES

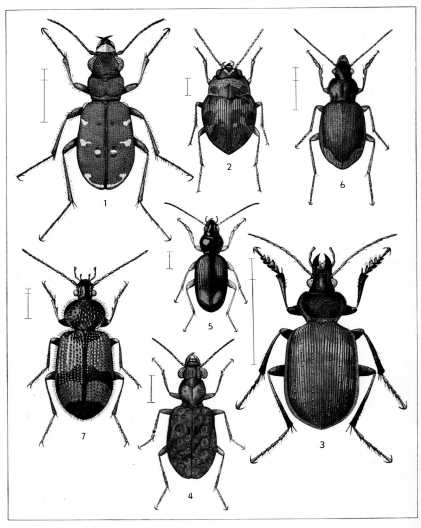

Colour Plate I

1 *Cicindela campestris* L., p. 54; 2 **Omophron limbatum* F., p. 54; 8 *Chlaenius vestitus* Payk.. p. 64; 4 *Bembidion ustulatum* L., p. 62; 5 *Panagaeus crux-major* L., p. 64; 6 *Elaphrus riparius* L., p. 56; 7 *Calosoma sycophanta* L., p. 56.

OPEN AIR GUIDES

BEETLES

BY

DR JAN BECHYNĚ

TRANSLATED AND EDITED BY

C. M. F. VON HAYEK

WITH OVER 250 ILLUSTRATIONS OF BEETLES

48 OF WHICH ARE IN COLOUR

FROM ORIGINALS BY B. BECHYNĚ

AND 59 DIAGRAMS

THAMES AND HUDSON

LONDON · NEW YORK

The original German edition was published by
Franckh'sche Verlagshandlung Stuttgart
under the title
WELCHER KÄFER IST DAS?

1956
All rights reserved
Printed and bound in Great Britain
by Jarrold and Sons Ltd Norwich

CONTENTS

COLOUR PLATES

PREFACE

THIS BOOK IS INTENDED to help all who are interested in Beetles to identify the specimens they find. No previous knowledge of the subject is assumed, and no use is made of the techniques available only to the specialist.

The Beetle fauna of Central Europe includes over 6,000 known species, of which over 3,600 occur in the British Isles. The majority of these species are very difficult to find unless one knows exactly what they look like and where to find them; partly because they are very small and the species often look very much alike, and partly because many species live in very specialized habitats, such as Ants' nests or on rare plants. A number of Beetles inhabit only very limited areas, for example the sea-shore or the tops of high mountains, and others are very rare. The remaining 300–400 species include the larger and more common Beetles: it is with these that this book is concerned.

From early spring to late autumn, Beetles may be found almost everywhere—in town and in the country, in the house and in the garden, in water, on the ground, under stones, in wood, under bark and under organic refuse.

Special technical terms are used in Entomology, the study of insects. The terms used in this book are the same as those found in the standard works on Beetles (Coleoptera). Each term is explained in the text, and there is a glossary of the terms used in the key at the back of the book.

The choice of species in this book is intended to give a picture of the more common British and European Beetles and to show how they are classified. The most recent classification is that proposed by R. Crowson which is based on the internal structure of the adult Beetle and on the characteristics of the larva. The use of this classification is, however, limited to the specialist assisted by a high-power microscope and specialized laboratory techniques. The classification used in this book is based on that found in Reitter's *Fauna Germanica*. This work is indispensable to anyone wishing to make a detailed study of the European Beetles.

Genera and species not occurring in the British Isles are marked with an asterisk.

The variations in size of the beetles shown in the figures are indicated by the rules to the side of the drawings. In every case the shortest measurement is the lower marked portion of the rule and the whole rule shows the maximum length.

B. AND J. BECHYNĚ

THE EXTERNAL STRUCTURE

(Morphology)

BEFORE WE CAN CONSIDER the British Beetles in detail, we must ask ourselves one question. How can we distinguish a Beetle from other insects, such as Cockroaches, Earwigs and Plant Bugs?

The body of a Beetle (Fig. A), like that of all other adult insects, is divided into three main parts: the head, the fore-body (thorax), and the hind-body (abdomen). The head bears the compound eyes and a pair of feelers (antennae). The thorax is composed of three rings or segments, each bearing a pair of legs. The abdomen consists of many segments, but it does not bear any appendages. These parts may vary greatly in size and shape, but the basic structure is always characteristic of the Beetle family. From above only the upper surface (pronotum) of the first thoracic segment (prothorax) is visible. The second segment (mesothorax) is entirely hidden by the two large curved wing-cases (elytra), which also cover the third thoracic segment (metathorax) and often the entire abdomen. The metathorax bears the membranous

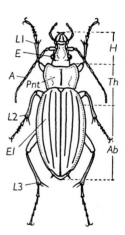

Fig. A. Outline drawing of a Ground Beetle (*Carabus auratus*). *A*, antenna; *Ab*, abdomen; *E*, eye; *El*, elytra; *H*, head; *L1*, *2*, *3*, front, mid and hind pairs of legs; *Pnt*, pronotum; *Th*, thorax. Original drawing by W. Söllner.

9

flight-wings which are folded away beneath the elytra when the Beetle is at rest. The picture presented is one of an insect with three conspicuous features; the head, the elytra and the legs.

But to make quite certain that our insect is a Beetle, we must learn to recognize its other characteristic features. Let us begin with the head.

The head is formed of a hard chitinous capsule, usually joined to the prothorax by a narrow neck (collum), and in this case it is freely movable. Sometimes, however, the head is deeply sunk into the prothorax, and it is then capable of only very little movement. The head is usually stretched forward, occasionally hanging down, and in some groups of Beetles it is at right angles to the longitudinal axis of the body—that is, hanging vertically. The head can undergo various modifications, for example in the Weevils the front of the head may be drawn out into a snout or rostrum, which may be long and thin or short and stout.

The mouth-parts (Fig. B) lie at the front of the head. In contrast with the piercing mouth-parts of the Mosquitoes, the Beetles have biting mouth-parts, consisting of well-developed jaws, working scissor-fashion from the sides, which enable

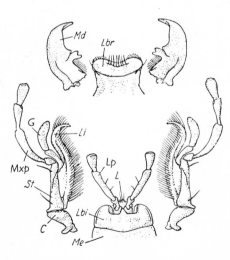

Fig. B. Mouth-parts of a Ground Beetle (*Carabus auratus*). *C*, cardo; *G*, galea; *L*, ligula; *Lbi*, labium; *Lbr*, labrum; *Li*, lacinia; *Lp*, labial palp; *Md*, mandible; *Me*, mentum; *Mxp*, maxillary palp; *St*, stipes. Original drawing by W. Söllner.

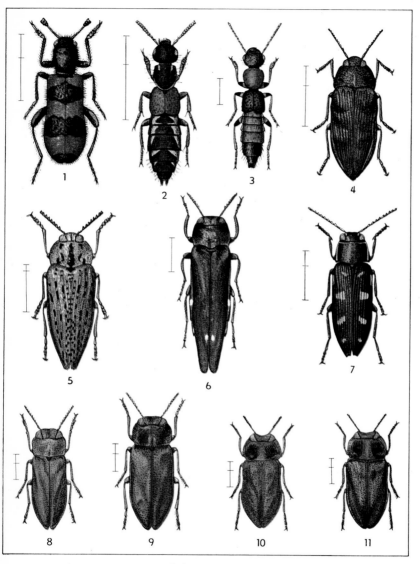

Colour Plate II

1 *Trichodes apiarius L., p. 81; 2 Staphylinus caesareus Cederh., p. 76;
3 Paederus littoralis Grav., p. 76; 4 *Buprestis rustica L., p. 86; 5 *Lampra
rutilans F., p. 86; 6 Agrilus biguttatus F., p. 88; 7 *Buprestis 8-guttata L.,
p. 88; 8 (♂) and 9(♀) Anthaxia nitidula L., p. 88; 10 (♂) and 11(♀)
*Anthaxia fulgurans F., p. 88.

them to break up their food
into small particles. In this
respect they resemble the
Cockroaches and their other
Grasshopper relations, which
also have biting mouth-
parts.

The roof of the mouth is
formed by a simple plate
(labrum) hinged to the front
of the head. Beneath the
labrum is a pair of stout jaws
(mandibles) which, in the
larger species, can inflict quite
a painful "bite". The mandibles may be greatly overgrown as in the male Stag
Beetle, where they resemble
antlers. Beneath the mandibles
lie the lower jaws (maxillae).
These are a more complicated
pair of organs with several
compound parts. Each one
consists of a small triangular
plate (cardo) to which a
slender stem (stipes) is joined.
The stipes bears an inner,
sickle-shaped lobe (lacinia)
and an outer, occasionally
segmented, lobe (galea). In
addition the stipes also bears

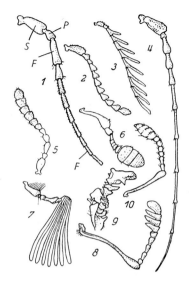

Fig. c. Different forms of antennae.
1, Ground Beetle (*Carabus auratus*);
2, Click Beetle (*Lacon murinus*);
3, Upland Click Beetle (*Corymbites pectinicornis*); 4, Longhorn Beetle
(*Cerambyx cerdo*); 5, Colorado
Potato Beetle (*Leptinotarsa decemlineata*); 6, Pine-Shoot Beetle
(*Blastophagus piniperda*); 7, Cockchafer (*Melolontha melolontha*);
8, Stag Beetle (*Lucanus cervus*);
9, Meloid (**Cercoma mühlfeldi*);
10, Weevil (**Liparus glabrirostris*).
F, flagellum; *P*, pedicel; *S*, scape.
After H. Eidmann and original
drawing by W. Söllner.

a four-segmented sensory appendage, the maxillary palp.
Finally, the floor of the mouth is formed by a compound
lower lip (labium); this is composed of a single median plate
(mentum) bearing an outer pair of three-segmented labial

11

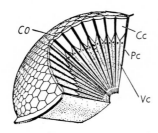

Fig. D. Diagram of a compound eye. *Cc*, crystalline cone; *Co*, corneal lens; *Pc*, pigment cell; *Vc*, visual cell. After A. Kuhn.

palpi, paired unsegmented plates (paraglossae)—which may be missing—and a single central plate (ligula), which is never missing.

The antennae (Fig. C) arise from the head behind the mouthparts; they may show considerable variety of form, and are sometimes very different in the two sexes. Fundamentally, they consist of a basal joint (scape), followed by the second joint (pedicel) which in turn bears the rest of the antenna (flagellum). The flagellum may vary greatly in form; it may be bristle-like (setaceous) thread-like (filiform), saw-like (serrate) on one or both sides, clubbed (clavate) or plated (lamellate). The antennae are organs of touch and smell and are therefore of great importance to the Beetles. The structure of the antennae varies with the relative importance of these senses.

Fig. E1. The divided compound eye of the Whirligig Beetle (*Gyrinus distinctus*). Original drawing by W. Söllner.

The visual organs of Beetles are the compound (or faceted) eyes (Fig. D) situated on either side of the head behind the antennae. These are usually hemispherical black organs built up of individual units (ommatidia), which may vary in number from a few to several thousand. The eyes, like the antennae and the mouth-parts, may be modified to serve several purposes. For example

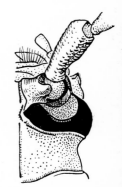

Fig. E2. The crescent-shaped eye of the Longhorn Beetle (*Cerambyx cerdo.*) Original drawing by W. Söllner.

12

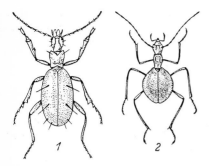

Fig. F. The cave-dwelling Beetles *Anopthalmus schmidti* (left) and *Leptodirus hohenwarthi* (right). From P. Grassé and after E. Rabaud.

the eyes of the Whirligig Beetle (Fig. E1) are divided into two parts, the upper being used for vision in air, and the lower for vision in water. In some male Longhorn Beetles the base of the antenna is almost completely surrounded by the eye (Fig. E2). In addition to the compound eyes some Beetles, for example the Bacon Beetle and the Omalinae, have one or two simple eyes (ocelli) on the forehead. Ocelli are also found in the Dragonflies, Grasshoppers and Flies.

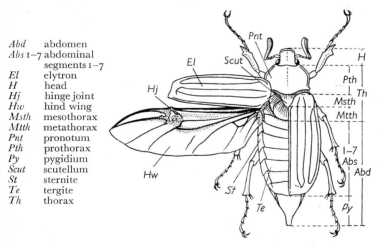

Abd	abdomen
Abs 1–7	abdominal segments 1–7
El	elytron
H	head
Hj	hinge joint
Hw	hind wing
Msth	mesothorax
Mtth	metathorax
Pnt	pronotum
Pth	prothorax
Py	pygidium
Scut	scutellum
St	sternite
Te	tergite
Th	thorax

Fig. G. Cockchafer (*Melolontha melolontha*). Left elytron and wing extended. Original drawing by W. Söllner.

13

Entirely blind Beetles, and Beetles with poorly developed eyes are found only among the cave-dwelling species (Fig. F). In compensation, however, these Beetles often have exceptionally long antennae and legs, bearing many long, sensitive hairs. Similar hairs may also be present on the elytra, pronotum and head.

We must now examine the parts of the body behind the head in greater detail. As we have already seen, the thorax consists of three segments (Fig. G), the prothorax, mesothorax and metathorax. Each segment has an upper and a lower chitinous plate, known as the tergite and sternite respectively. In all Beetles the tergum of the prothorax takes the form of a flat plate (pronotum). A small, strongly chitinized plate (scutellum), lying behind the pronotum and between the elytra, is the only part of the metathoracic segment visible from above when the insect is at rest. The upper appendages of the mesothorax, the elytra, are however very conspicuous. These structures are developed from sac-like lateral lobes of the mesothorax, and they may be

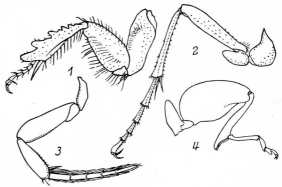

Fig. H. Legs of Beetles. 1, left fore-leg of a Dor Beetle (*Geotrupes stercorarius*), used for digging; 2, right hind-leg of a Ground Beetle (*Carabus auratus*), used for walking; 3, right hind-leg of a Water Beetle (*Dytiscus marginalis*), used for swimming; 4, left hind-leg of a Flea Beetle (*Psylliodes affinis*), used for jumping. Original drawing by W. Söllner.

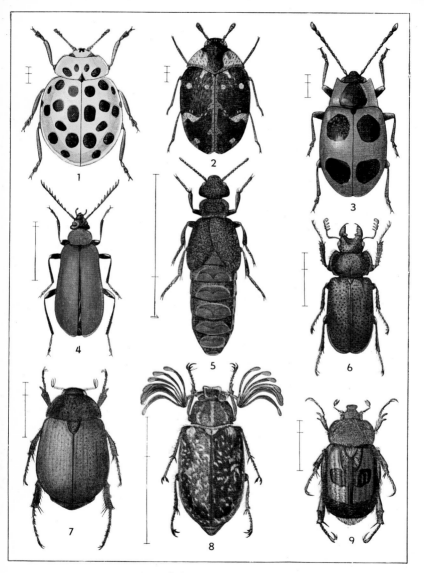

Colour Plate III

1 *Thea 22-punctata* L., p. 97; 2 *Anthrenus scrophulariae* L., p. 98; 3 *Endomychus coccineus* L., p. 96; 4 *Pyrochroa coccinea* L. (Cardinal Beetle), p. 104; 5 *Meloë variegatus* Donov., p. 106; 6 **Systenocerus caraboides* L., p. 108; 7 *Anomala aenea* Deg., p. 114; 8 **Polyphylla fullo* F. [Walker], p. 113; 9 *Anisoplia agricola* Poda., p. 113.

very strongly chitinized. The elytra completely cover the mesothorax and the metathorax, and often the whole abdomen.

The membranous hind wings (alae) are developed from similar lobes of the metathorax. When the Beetle is at rest they are folded lengthways and crosswise and stowed away beneath the elytra. All Beetles, with the exception of the Rose Chafers and their allies (Cetoniinae), fly with the elytra held erect. The elytra of the Chafers remain closed, but they are cut away on either side in front to allow

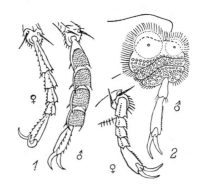

Fig. 1. Feet (tarsal segments) of Beetles. 1, tarsal segments of the front leg of female (♀) and male (♂) Ground Beetle (*Carabus auratus*, ♀ with spines, ♂ with pubescent sole; 2, tarsal segments of the front leg of female (♀) and male (♂) Water Beetle (*Dytiscus marginalis*), ♂ with two large and numerous small suckers. After H. Eidmann.

free movement of the wings. The elytra are often shortened so that a varying number of abdominal segments may be exposed. This is particularly noticeable in the Rove Beetles (Staphylinidae) and the Oil Beetles (*Meloë*). The elytra are entirely absent in the flightless females of the Glow-worm (*Lampyris noctiluca*).

Each thoracic segment bears on its underside a pair of jointed legs (Fig. H). Each leg has the following parts: first, a basal piece (coxa) which forms a joint with the sternite. The coxa is joined to the thigh (femur) by a small intermediate part (trochanter). The femur is followed by the shin (tibia), which in turn carries the segmented foot (tarsus). The last tarsal segment bears a pair of claws. Many modifications of the legs exist to suit various ways of life. The Dung Beetles have short spiny legs for digging, the True Water Beetles have oar-like swimming legs, and the jumping Flea Beetles have thickened femora to accommodate the muscles used in jumping. The tarsi may also be modified to suit various purposes. These are often in the form of clasping organs in the male (Fig. 1).

The segments following the metathorax form the abdomen. These segments also have upper and lower chitinous plates (abdominal tergites and sternites), but in this case only the latter are strongly chitinized. The first few tergites are usually membranous as the elytra afford protection to the internal organs in this region. Only the last few tergites, and especially the pygidium which is usually exposed, are strongly chitinized. The pygidium of the Cockchafers is very conspicuous, being drawn out into a long, spiny process. Some Nitidulidae have an additional segment behind the pygidium, but this is present only in the males.

THE INTERNAL STRUCTURE
(Anatomy)

Having formed a general picture of the external appearance of a Beetle, we must now examine its internal structure.

Let us dissect a large Beetle, for example the Great Water Beetle (*Dytiscus marginalis*). To do this, we first cut off the elytra, and then pin down the Beetle in a dissecting-dish (a shallow dish with a layer of wax at the bottom) so that its underside is touching the bottom. The dish is then filled with sufficient water to cover the insect. Next, using a sharp-pointed pair of scissors, we make two cuts through the tergites; one up the right-hand side, and the other up the left-hand side of the abdomen and thorax. The tergites are then carefully lifted away from the underlying structures. A triangular cut is made in the upper surface of the head between the eyes.

The first thing noticed on opening the insect is the closely coiled intestine. Above the intestine, and immediately below the tergites, is the long, tubular heart (Fig. J) with its lateral openings. In the living insect the pulsation of the

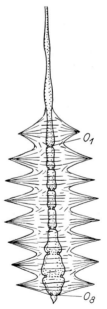

Fig. J. Heart and aorta of *Dytiscus marginalis*. O_1–O_8, ostia. After W. Kuhl.

17

heart draws the colourless blood through these openings (ostia) and drives it forwards into the aorta. From the aorta the blood is again returned to the body cavity. Beetles do not have an elaborate system of blood-vessels.

But to return to the dissection. The intestine (Fig. κ) consists of a short, tubular oesophagus leading to the thin-walled crop, followed in turn by the muscular gizzard. The walls of the gizzard are armed with horny ridges, spines and teeth. In the giz-

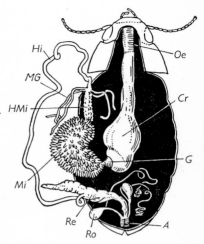

Fig. κ. Alimentary canal of *Dytiscus marginalis*. *A*, anus; *Cr*, crop; *G*, gizzard; *Hi*, hind-intestine; *HMi*, hind portion of mid-intestine; *Mi*, mid-intestine; *MG*, Malpighian tubules; *Oe*, oesophagus; *Re*, rectum; *Ro*, reproductive organs. After Rungius from Grassé.

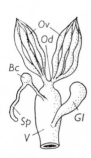

Fig. L. Female reproductive organs of a Beetle (diagrammatic). *Bc*, bursa copulatrix; *Gl*, gland; *Od*, oviduct; *Ov*, ovarioles; *Sp*, spermatheca; *V*, vagina. After H. Weber.

zard the food, already partly broken down by the mouth-parts, undergoes further crushing and grinding. The food then passes through a strainer (proventriculus) which allows only liquid food to pass into the mid-intestine. The mid-intestine may be divided into two regions, an anterior and a posterior mid-intestine; it is mainly in the latter that the food is absorbed. The mid-intestine is followed in turn by the long, thin hind-intestine and the enlarged rectum which opens to the exterior by the anus. Four to six thin coiled tubes open into the intestine at the point where the mid-intestine joins the hind-intestine; these are the Malpighian tubules which function as the kidneys of the Beetle.

In female specimens two groups of short tubules, each leading to a common duct, can be seen at the posterior end of the abdomen (Fig. L). These are the ovarioles and oviducts. The right and left oviducts join to form a wider passage, the uterus. Two small organs, the sperm pouch (receptaculum seminis) and the cement gland, open into the uterus. The receptaculum seminis is a pouch for the reception and storage of the spermatozoa. The cement glands secrete a sticky substance which serves to fasten the eggs to sticks, leaves, etc.

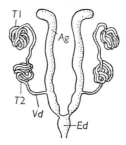

Fig. M. Male reproductive organs of a Beetle (diagrammatic). *Ag*, accessory gland; *Ed*, ejaculatory duct; *T1*, *T2*, testes; *Vd*, vas deferens. Adapted from H. Weber.

The internal genital organs of the male (Fig. M) are much less conspicuous. The testes are two small paired globular organs lying at the posterior end of the abdomen. Paired ducts (vasa deferentia) run from the testes and join to form the single ejaculatory duct leading to the external genital organ, the aedeagus. The aedeagus of the large Ground Beetles has the appearance of a stout hook turned to the left.

The central nervous system (Fig. N) can only be seen when the

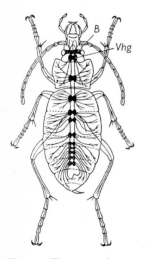

Fig. N. The central nervous system of a Ground Beetle (*Carabus auratus*). *B*, brain; *Vhg*, ventral head ganglion. Adapted from J. du Val.

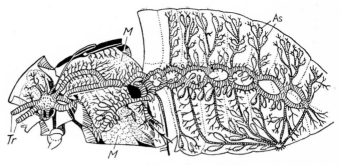

Fig. o. The tracheal system of a Cockchafer (*Melolontha melolontha*). *As*, air sacs; *M*, muscle fibres; *Tr*, tracheae. After Straus-Dürckheim.

intestine and the reproductive organs have been removed. Careful examination will reveal that it consists of two thin, creamy-white nerve cords joined at intervals by swellings (ganglia). From the ganglia small nerves run out to the various parts of the body. The ventral head-ganglion or suboesophageal ganglion is even larger than the relatively large thoracic ganglia; it supplies nerves to the mouth-parts. The suboesophageal ganglion is connected to the supraoesophageal ganglion or brain by nerves running round the oesophagus. The brain supplies nerves to the eyes and all the other sensory organs of the head.

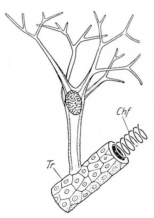

Fig. p. Structure of a trachea. *Chf*, chitin filament; *Tr*, trachea. After H. Weber.

Numerous bundles of white fibres running parallel to one another may be seen in the body cavity, and especially in the thorax. These are the muscle fibres which are especially well developed in strongly-flying insects.

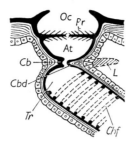

Fig. Q. Longitudinal section of a spiracle. *At*, atrium; *Cb*, closing bow; *Cbd*, closing band; *Chf*, chitin filament; *L*, closing lever; *Oc*, outer chamber; *Pr*, fringed processes of lips; *Tr*, trachea. After H. Weber.

Insects have no lungs and breathe by means of a system of air-tubes or tracheae (Fig. o), which form a fine network around the internal organs of the body. Tracheae (Fig. p) are fine tubes strengthened on the inside by a tight spiral of chitin. The air enters the tracheae through paired openings (spiracles or stigmata) which can be clearly seen on either side of the abdomen. From the spiracle (Fig. q) a short trachea runs into the body where it divides into an anterior and a posterior branch, from which fine branches run to all parts of the body. In strongly-flying insects the fine branches often terminate in small swellings or air-sacs. These air-sacs are inflated, before every flight, by pumping movements of the abdomen. These respiratory movements are often seen in the Cockchafers just before they take wing.

Finally, we must mention the irregular mass of cells which occupies much of the space around the internal organs. These cells form the so-called fat-body of the Beetle and serve for the storage of reserve food substances.

THE DEVELOPMENT OF A BEETLE
(Ontogeny)

BEETLES, LIKE ALL OTHER ANIMALS, hatch from eggs. Ripe eggs from the ovary pass down the oviduct into the uterus, where they are fertilized by sperm from the receptaculum seminis. The eggs are usually laid on or near the food of the larva. The larva which emerges from the egg does not look at all like the adult Beetle, but the structure of the larva is always characteristic of the species to which it belongs.

A Beetle larva (Fig. R) has a head and a twelve-segmented

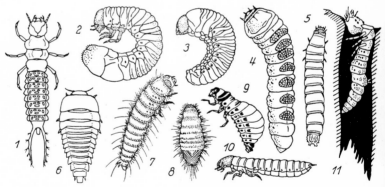

Fig. R. Beetle larvae. 1, Ground Beetle; 2, Cockchafer (*Melolontha melolontha*); 3, Pine-Shoot Beetle (*Blastophagus piniperda*); 4, Longhorn Beetle (*Cerambyx cerdo*); 5, Click Beetle (*Corymbites aeneus*); 6, Carrion Beetle; 7, Bacon Beetle (*Dermestes lardarius*); 8, Museum Beetle (*Anthrenus verbasci*); 9, Colorado Potato Beetle (*Leptinotarsa decemlineata*); 10, *Dascillus* species; 11, Tiger Beetle (*Cicindela campestris*). After H. Eidmann, E. Reitter and H. Weber.

body, whose first three segments may each bear a pair of legs. The mouth-parts of the larva are very similar to those of the adult, but of a less complicated structure; the mandibles, maxilla and labium are always present. The larvae do not possess compound eyes, but they may have one to six simple eyes or ocelli. The antennae are short, having fewer segments than those of the adult. Characteristic larval organs, that is, structures present only in the larval stage, are often found on the last abdominal or anal segment. These structures (cerci) may be in the form of long, spiny, paired appendages, like those of the May-flies, or they may be short, stout, hook-like structures, used by the insect for attaching itself to its food plant. Similar structures are also found in the caterpillar larvae of Butterflies, which are in every way comparable to Beetle larvae.

The entire life of the larva is devoted to searching for food and feeding. It is, therefore, not surprising that the structure of the larva is closely related to the food it eats, and the way in which it obtains it. The predacious Ground Beetle (Carabid) and Tiger Beetle (Cicindelid) larvae have slender bodies and long legs; these larvae actively hunt their prey. The larvae of the wood-feeding Longhorn Beetles (Cerambycidae), the Dung Beetles (Geotrupidae) and the parasitic Oil Beetles (*Meloë*), which have food in plenty all around them, have thick, soft bodies with short legs, or the legs may be missing altogether. By examining the larva carefully, it is often possible to deduce the kind of food it eats.

If sufficient food is available, the larva increases rapidly in size, but only so far as the hard and inelastic skin or cuticle will allow. To overcome this, a new skin is formed beneath the old one, which then splits open down the back and allows the larva to emerge. The new skin is at first soft and has a much-folded surface allowing for a further increase in size. This process of moulting (ecdysis) is repeated three or four times before the larva is full-grown.

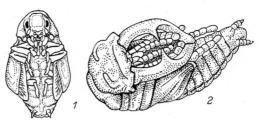

Fig. s. Beetle pupae. 1, Pine-Shoot Beetle (*Blastophagus piniperda*); 2, Male Stag Beetle (*Lucanus cervus*). After H. Eidmann and Rösel von Rosenhof.

When the larva has reached its full size it stops feeding, and after the last moult it becomes an immobile pupa (Fig. s). Although the pupa is apparently quiescent, many changes are going on inside, and soon the structures characteristic of the adult Beetle can be seen: the head becomes distinct, and in the Stag Beetle the "antlers" may be seen. The legs and antennae are folded together on the underside.

When the time comes for the adult insect to emerge, the pupal skin splits down the back and the soft-skinned young Beetle appears. At first the insect-skin is soft and yellow, but in a few hours it hardens and acquires the typical colours of the species.

This kind of development, in which the form emerging from the egg is very different in appearance from the adult and must pass through successive larval and pupal stages before reaching the adult form, is known as a complete metamorphosis. Some insects, such as the Grasshoppers, Termites and Bugs (Hemiptera) undergo an incomplete metamorphosis: they hatch out of the egg in a form closely resembling the adult, and grow directly into the adult by a series of moults: there is no pupal stage.

The length of the life-cycle, from egg to adult, through the larval and pupal stages, varies according to the species, and the kind of food it eats. In some species the life-cycle is very short, so that there may be two, three or even more generations in one year. In other species the larval stage may last several years; for example three to four years in the Cockchafer and five to six years in the Stag Beetle. These are known as three-to-four, and five-to-six year cycles, and are the explanation of the so-called "Cockchafer plagues" which may occur every three to four years. The length of larval life is very often related to the nature of the food. For example, Longhorn larvae feeding on wood, which has a low nutrient value, have a very long larval life. On the other hand, the larval life of species living on green plants is never longer than one year. The development, from egg to adult, of the predacious species is also fairly rapid.

In comparison to the long larval life of the wood-feeding larvae of the Stag Beetle, the life of the adult is very short, being very rarely longer than a few weeks. The short life of the adult Beetle is solely concerned—apart from feeding— with the maintenance and dispersal of its kind. A few Beetles show some degree of parental care, for example the Dung Beetles, which provide food for their young.

like the Colorado Potato Beetle, they may become serious pests.

In many cases certain events in the history of the Earth have resulted in insects becoming established in regions which they would not have reached otherwise. During the Ice Age, when the Northern Hemisphere was covered with ice, many northern species were forced southwards—some as far as the Alps, by the advancing ice. A few of these northern species were able to establish themselves, and remained in these new regions when the ice retreated. As the ice retreated the distributional range spread northwards again, and eventually only small populations of the northern species remained in the Alps, where the environmental conditions were similar to those of their original northern home. These species were unable to establish themselves in the plains left by the retreating ice and are not found there. This is known as the Boreo-Alpine type of distribution.

The land from which the ice retreated did not remain uninhabited, but was recolonized by insects—especially those able to run and fly strongly—from the regions to which they had withdrawn during the Ice Age. Beetles which found suitable habitats soon became established. After the Ice Age many Mediterranean species also invaded Europe: these were partly species whose present-day centre of distribution is still the steppe regions north of the Black Sea (Pontic species) and partly species which had found shelter on the relatively warm Atlantic seaboard during the Ice Age. Others came from the Mediterranean coast (Mediterranean species), either from the western Mediterranean coast (Western Mediterranean species) or from the Balkans (Eastern Mediterranean species). Together all these species form the present-day Beetle fauna of Central Europe.

It seems probable that most of the British species, or their ancestors, invaded the British Isles from abroad, either from Europe or from other parts of the world.

Even today we can discover the centre of distribution of a species if we know the kind of habitat in which it lives, and also its complete distributional range. For example, the western boundary of the Pontic species, which favour a warm, dry climate, is at that point where the climate becomes damp (Atlantic). Similarly the eastern boundary of the Atlantic species lies where the Atlantic climate with its warm, damp summers and comparatively mild winters gives place to the dry summers and cold winters of the east.

As Eastern Continental species are found in dry places in regions which have an Atlantic climate, and Atlantic species are found in eastern Continental regions, it may be presumed that the former became established when the Continental climate extended farther west, and the latter when the Atlantic climate extended farther east. These small groups of species or individuals found in very limited areas of widely separated regions are known as Relict Faunas. According to their origin they are known as Atlantic, Pontic or Arctic Relicts, and according to their habitat they are classed as stenotope thermophiles, psammophiles, etc.

If we wish to investigate the structure and probable origin of the present-day Beetle fauna of a district we must undertake the following three tasks:

1. Work out the distribution of the Beetles within the district. This task is of a purely faunistic nature, accumulating facts from field work.
2. Study the relations of the Beetles to their habitat, that is, their ecology.
3. Discover the general distribution of the various species, both in the British Isles and on the Continent. This task is purely zoogeographical.

The same factors which limit the horizontal distribution

of a species will also affect its vertical distribution. In mountainous regions the species from the low-lying areas are not found above a certain height on the mountain-side, and the mountain-top species are usually missing from the valleys. This limitation of the vertical range of a species may be so marked that some species are found only at certain altitudes, and we may distinguish between the following groups: hill-side species (colline), mountain species (montane), pinewood-region species (subalpine) and snow-line species (nivale).

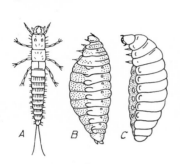

Fig. T. Larval stages of the Oil Beetle (*Meloë*). *A*, triungulin larva; *B*, 2nd stage larva; *C*, 3rd stage larva. After E. Reitter.

The species that live on the surface of the ground and seek shelter under stones, in decaying wood and in the upper layers of the soil only by day or in times of drought are to be distinguished from those species that always live underground; many of the cave-dwelling species (Cavernicoles) belong to this second group. In the more northerly parts of Europe most of the Cavernicoles became extinct during the Ice Age, and they are now only found in any numbers in southern Europe. The special characteristics of this group are mentioned on pages 13–14; in addition they are often lacking in pigment. Colourless albino species also occur elsewhere, especially in the more extreme types of habitat such as the snow-line regions. Cases of darkening of the ground-colour (melanism) and multiplication of black markings (nigrism) occur more frequently.

We must now consider two of the more important ecological groups, the parasites and the symbionts.

Parasites live in or on the bodies of other animals, known

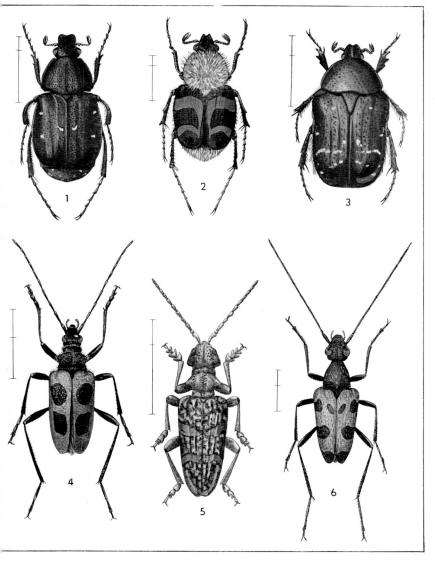

Colour Plate IV

1 *Gnorimus nobilis* L., p. 114; 2 *Trichius fasciatus* L. (Bee Beetle), p. 116;
3 *Cetonia aurata* L. (Rose Chafer), p. 112; 4 *Pachyta 4-maculata* L., p. 118;
5 *Rhagium sycophanta* Schr., p. 117; 6 *Judolia cerambyciformis* Schr., p. 118.

as their hosts. The larva of the Oil Beetle (*Meloë*) is parasitic on Bees. It is of special interest to note that as an adaptation to a parasitic mode of life, a specialized type of larva has been evolved. This larva (Fig. 1*A*), called a triungulin because of the extra claw on each leg, lurks on flowers until an opportunity occurs for it to attach itself to the hairs on the body of a Bee. When it reaches the nest it changes into a short, fat-bodied, short-legged larva (Fig. 1*B*, *C*), which feeds on the food intended for the Bee larvae, and occasionally also on the larvae and eggs.

Symbionts are animals which live in a close relationship (symbiosis) with other animals, to their mutual benefit. The relationship between Ants and some of their guests is of this kind. Ant guests may be divided into four groups. The first group includes the trophobionts; these are either guests which seek the Ants, or else animals actively sought by the Ants. The trophobionts produce a sweet secretion which serves as food for their hosts, but the Ants do not feed or care for the trophobionts in any way. Such is the relationship between Ants and Plant-lice, some Bugs and the Caterpillars of the "Blue" Butterflies. The true Ant guests or symphiles form the second group, and they are distinguished by tufts of hair (trichomes) surrounding some glands which produce a secretion much loved by the Ants. The Ants feed and protect the adults and rear the larvae of the symphiles. Species of the genera *Paussus*, *Lomechusa* and *Atemeles* belong to this group. The third and largest group includes the tolerated lodgers or synoeketes. These species are tolerated for several reasons, they may have a hard, shiny body-armour which makes them difficult to attack successfully, or else they may be able to defend themselves against the Ants. Many species of the Staphylinid genus *Dinarda* belong to this group; they are chiefly scavengers feeding on nest refuse. The fourth group, the synechthrans, are carnivorous Staphylinid Beetles of the genus *Quedius* which prey on the Ants and their larvae. The Ants actively attack these unwelcome guests and try to eject them from the nest.

The phenomena of symbiosis and parasitism demonstrate that insects must not be regarded as entirely independent individuals, but as members of a community (biocoenosis) together with other animals and plants. The individual members of the community are in a state of balance with one another; the removal of one species can upset the equilibrium of a whole biocoenosis. The introduction of a strange species or a change in the temperature or in the height of the water-table can destroy an entire community.

A great deal of work still remains to be done on the life-history and ecology of many British species. When a Beetle is found a careful note should be made of the conditions under which it was found; the kind of plant on which it lived, the time of day at which it was active, and whether it was found in a dry, damp or salty place. Living insects should be observed to see where and how they lay their eggs and where they hide by day or night. In addition Beetle larvae should be taken home and reared to maturity. All these observations should be entered in a journal, and any material obtained in the course of breeding out a species, such as larval and pupal skins (exuvia) and frass (refuse left by larvae) should be carefully preserved. In this way it may be possible to add something to the knowledge of the bionomics of Beetles.

NAMING AND CLASSIFICATION
(Nomenclature and Systematics)

IN THE COURSE OF A WALK through the fields one may find Beetles on the edge of the path, sweep them from leaves and flowers or catch them in flight. If we look at these Beetles carefully we shall see that they differ in size and shape and in the way they behave and move. Here, for example, a large Dor Beetle with shining black elytra creeps slowly over the ground, there a Click Beetle which has fallen on its back leaps into the air and lands upon its feet, and a Longhorn Beetle with antennae as long as its body sits quietly on a flower. It is possible to arrange the Beetles in groups according to their external characteristics, such as the shape of the legs, the structure of the antennae and the shape, length and structure of the elytra. Within a group the insects are more or less alike, but every group has certain distinguishing characteristics. The more each group is split up, the more the members of each small group will resemble one another, until finally a stage is reached when it is impossible to distinguish one specimen from another. If it were possible to observe such identical "kinds" of Beetle mating, it might reasonably be assumed that they belonged to the same species. The species is the starting-point of systematics, and the lowest category in the classification of Beetles, in fact of all Animals and Plants.

The world fauna of Beetles includes over half a million described species, of which over 3,600 occur in the British Isles. If distinctions were made only between the individual species it would not be possible to form any picture of the enormous diversity of form found in the Beetle family. A clearer picture will be obtained if the species which show certain characteristics in common are grouped together to form the next category in the ascending scale, the genus. A genus may include any number of species, sometimes only 1 or 2, more often 3, 4, 10 or 20, and occasionally 100 or more. It is often convenient to divide a large genus into subgenera according to the similarity and presumed relationship between the species.

It is not sufficient to group the species into genera; for convenience of reference each species requires a name. The system of naming which is used for Beetles and all other living things was first consistently used by the Swedish naturalist Carl von Linnaeus. He gave every animal two names, a generic name, usually derived from Latin or Greek and starting with a capital letter, and a specific name also derived from one of these languages and (almost always) printed in small letters. For example, he named the common Violet Ground Beetle *Carabus violaceus*, and its handsome but rare metallic-green relation *Carabus nitens*. As Linnaeus was the first to name them and publish a short paragraph stating how they differed from one another, his name, or the accepted abbreviation L., is quoted after the specific name. The full scientific name of the Violet Ground Beetle is therefore *Carabus violaceus* L., and that of its relation *Carabus nitens* L.

It may be asked why animals have been given names from the "Dead" languages. The reasons are:

1. Many Beetles have no common name.
2. If each worker was entitled to choose a name in his own language other workers might not be able to understand it.

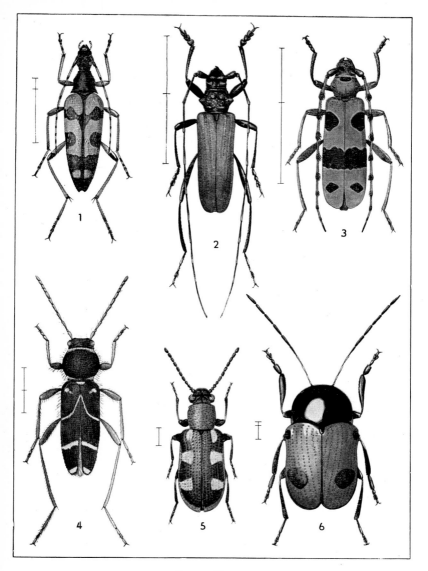

Colour Plate V

1 *Strangalia maculata Poda, p. 118; 2 Aromia moschata L. (Musk Beetle),
p. 120; 3 *Rosalia alpina L., p. 122; 4 *Clytus rhamni Germ., p. 120;
5 Crioceris asparagi L. (Asparagus Beetle), p. 126; 6 Cryptocephalus bipunctatus
L., p. 126.

3. Until quite recently, Latin was the language used by scientific workers all over the world, and it was therefore natural to use it for naming animals. The descriptions were also given in Latin.

This system (binomial) of giving each animal two names, first used by Linnaeus, has become an internationally accepted rule. When a new species is discovered, it is given a latinized specific name and placed in the genus containing its nearest relations. The name and description of the new species (n. sp.) must be published. In any later reference to the species the name of the describer is quoted after the specific name, thus: *Carabus monilis* Fab. (=Fabricius). If it is not possible to incorporate the species in a known genus a new genus (n. gen.) must be erected for it. With increased knowledge it is sometimes found that a species has been placed in the wrong genus; for example, *Carabus sycophanta* L., described as a member of the genus *Carabus*, later had to be placed in the genus *Calosoma*. In such a case the name of the original author of the species is then placed in brackets after the new combination of names thus: *Calosoma sycophanta* (L.).

The International Commission on Zoological Nomenclature has laid down a series of Rules of Nomenclature which are binding to all systematists. The Commission also decides on the validity of zoological names. One of the most important rules laid down by the Commission is the Law of Priority. This states that of all the names given to one species, the name which must be accepted is the one published first, even if it only precedes the other names for the same species by a page or a line. Different names for the same species are known as synonyms, and similar names for different species as homonyms. Names published before 1758, the date of publication of the tenth edition of Linnaeus' *Systema Naturae* in which the binomial system was first consistently used, are not taken into consideration.

35

When a new species is named, a description and a diagnosis, that is, a statement of how it differs from closely related species, must be published. The specimen, or one of the specimens before the author at the time of the description must be designated as the Type. This specimen must be carefully preserved (preferably in a museum or other scientific institution) so that if necessary the description can be checked against the type. It quite frequently happens that two or more species have to be united because the original authors did not realize the full extent of the variation within the species.

At this stage it will be convenient to give a short account of the variations found within species. Very often there is a considerable difference between the two sexes of one species: the male Stag Beetle has a large head and antler-like mandibles, whereas the head and jaws of the female are small. Considerable variations in colour and other characteristics may be shown by individuals of the same species and sex. For example the number and arrangement of the spots of the common two-spot Ladybird *Adalia bipunctata* L. may vary a great deal (Fig. u). Several different varieties (abbreviated to var.) may occur in the same locality. These varieties are known as aberrations or forms and if they are given names these are preceded by ab. or f. The four-spotted form of the two-spot Ladybird could be named *Adalia bipunctata* ab. *quadripunctata*, but it is advisable not to use these names as they have no validity under the Rules of Nomenclature, nor are they available under the Law of Priority. Sometimes the individuals of a species in one part of the country may be distinguished from those in a distant part. These groups are regarded as geographical races or subspecies (abbreviated to ssp.). The fact that intermediate forms do exist in the regions where the two subspecies meet proves that the two subspecies belong to the same species. Each subspecies is given an additional name, so

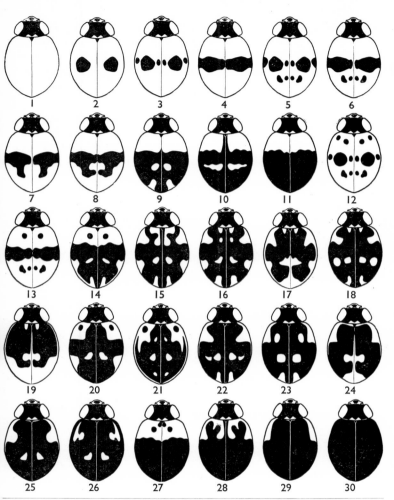

Fig. u. Colour varieties of the Ladybird Beetle *Adalia bipunctata* L. Original drawing by B. Bechyně.

1 ab. *concolor*, 2 f. *typica*, 3 ab. *boreella*, 4 ab. *unifasciata*, 5 ab. *friederikae*, 6 ab. *olivieri*, 7 ab. *häneli*, 8 ab. *annulata*, 9 ab. *subsexpustulata*, 10 ab. *transversa*, 11 ab. *seminigra*, 12 ab. *simulatrix*, 13 ab. *marshami*, 14 ab. *fraudulenta*, 15 ab. *similata*, 16 ab. *duodecimpustulata*, 17 ab. *hastata*, 18 ab. *octopustulata*, 19 ab. *haupti*, 20 ab. *subparens*, 21 ab. *mephisto*, 22 ab. *discedens*, 23 ab. *lineata*, 24 ab. *hastatoides*, 25 ab. *quadrimaculata*, 26 ab. *interrupta*, 27 ab. *semiatra*, 28 ab. *circumducta*, 29 ab. *sublunata*, 30 ab. *lugubris*.

37

that the binomial name becomes trinomial. In Britain the Staphylinid *Philonthus varius* has black elytra and is given the name *Philonthus varius varius*, while in the Shetlands and Orkneys the elytra are red; this subspecies is known as *Philonthus varius shetlandica*. In other groups—for instance in Ants and Man—even a trinomial system is insufficient to distinguish between the different groups, and quadrinomial (4), quinquenomial (5) and even sexnomial (6) names may be used. These categories are never used in the classification of Beetles.

Having glanced at the lower systematic groups we must pass on to the higher categories, that is, all those above the rank of genus. The next category in the ascending scale is the family, which includes all closely related genera. Related families are grouped together to form an order, and this is the highest group in the classification of Beetles. The order Coleoptera includes all the Beetles. It is often convenient to subdivide very large orders, such as the Coleoptera, into suborders, family groups or superfamilies, subfamilies and tribes.

The classification of a Ground Beetle may be shown in tabular form, thus:

Order: Coleoptera (Beetles)
  Suborder: Adephaga (Carnivores)
    Family group or Superfamily: Caraboidea (Ground
        Beetle-like species)
      Family: Carabidae (Ground Beetles)
       Subfamily: Carabinae
        Tribe: Carabini
         Genus: *Carabus*
          Subgenus: *Megadontus*
           Species: *Carabus (Megadontus) violaceus* L.
             (The Violet Ground Beetle)
             Subspecies: *Carabus (Megadontus) violaceus solicitans* Hart. The British
                subspecies

This is known as a Natural System of Classification, that is, one based on the degree of relationship. The aim of modern systematics is not only to give a picture of the diversity of animal forms and to provide a means of identifying them, but also to give a picture of the phylogenetic relationships.

WHERE ARE BEETLES FOUND?

THE ANSWER TO THIS general question is simple: wherever there is a suitable habitat. As there are Beetles adapted to every kind of habitat, from the sea-shore to the snow-line of the highest mountains and from the poles to the equator, they are in fact to be found everywhere—except in the sea. A few species are ubiquitous, that is, one can find them everywhere if one looks for them at the right time of the year. However, if one wants to find a particular species one must first find out as much as one can about its life-history, its food, its distribution and so on. The successful capture of a special insect species depends not only on the knowledge of its life-history, but also on a host of other factors, such as the locality and the weather conditions. Chance also plays quite an important part, and it should not be forgotten that many a rare species has been found through sheer "Beginner's Luck".

Planticoles (see page 26) are found only on plants; they are usually monophagous, that is, they eat only one kind of plant, and often only certain parts of it such as the leaves, flowers or stems. These food-plants often have a limited distribution and may be very difficult to find. Very often when the food-plant has at last been found, the most careful search will fail to reveal the species expected, even though it is the right time of the year and the weather is suitable. The non-appearance of the species may be due to a number of reasons; the position of the plant may be too sunny, or too much in the shade, it may even be that certain plants in the vicinity are, for some reason, preventing the Beetles from

40

seeking their food-plants. The occurrence of certain Ground Beetles is dependent on a number of factors; these include the size of the sand-grains, the salt content of the ground and the availability of prey. From this it will be understood that many factors must be taken into account when deciding whether a species is likely to be found in a certain locality.

All the Beetles associated with a particular type of habitat will be found in that habitat, but only if it fulfils all their requirements. A carcass is an ideal habitat, and will soon harbour an entire community of carrion-feeders; numerous Dung Beetles (*Geotrupes* and many Staphylinidae) will converge upon fresh cow-dung. But once the decay has reached a certain stage, or the dung has dried out, the invasion of these species ceases and others take their place. The Beetle guests of Ants are influenced by many different factors. These include the season of the year, the amount of sunshine on the nest, the humidity, the presence of certain fungal mycelia in the nest, and also the vigour of the Ant colony itself.

It is impossible here to give detailed collecting instructions for every kind of habitat, and we shall therefore confine ourselves to general observations. Experience has shown that regions of very ancient rock-formations are poorer in species than the more recent limestone and Tertiary formations. Natural vegetation offers more species than cultivated areas. The "best" localities are small plant communities, as there the insects as well as the plants are more concentrated; collecting is also easier in these limited areas.

In southern Central Europe the southern slopes are richest in species, as it is there that representatives of southern species will occur in addition to the local fauna.

Edges of paths, rubbish-heaps and similar places are often rich in numbers but poor in species.

In sandy places, such as sand-dunes, Beetles will be found

buried more or less deeply in the sand, and also under wind-blown refuse and at plant roots.

Flood-refuse is particularly rich in insect life; many interesting finds have been made in such material, including species swept down from high altitudes.

It is well worth searching under stones, as many species take refuge there during the day and in times of drought. The stone must of course be returned to its original position, so that the other living things beneath it will not dry up or die of exposure to direct sunlight.

Stamping on the sandy banks of streams and lakes will often bring to light many small Staphylinidae and Heteroceridae (and also *Omophron limbatum F.).

Bark, moss and lichen should be carefully examined, both during the summer and winter months. It is pointless to search under the bark of healthy trees, and in any case, one must avoid causing any damage to standing timber. On the other hand one should search carefully under the bark of dead and decaying timber. Fungi also harbour a number of interesting species. There are in fact very few places which will not repay a careful search with some worth-while species.

In addition to these natural habitats, artificial ones may be specially created. Such habitats may be prepared by placing decaying meat, hides, bones, plant remains, or any other organic material in the sun or shade, or by burying them. The larger Ground Beetles can often be trapped with empty snail-shells. Pitfall traps, especially those in forests, are often a source of many different kinds of Beetles. The Beetles fall into the traps and are unable to escape because they cannot climb the smooth, vertical walls. Interesting species may also be found on the walls and floors of war-time shelters and trenches.

So far we have only been concerned with individual habitats. We must now consider a larger area, a meadow,

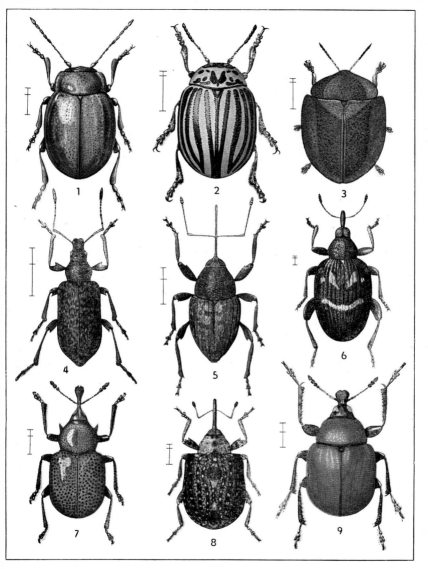

Colour Plate VI

1 *Dlochrysa fastuosa* Scop., p. 127; 2 *Leptinotarsa 10-lineata* Say (Colorado
Potato Beetle), p. 127; 3 *Cassida viridis* L. (Tortoise Beetle), p. 130;
4 *Phyllobius calcaratus* F. (Leaf Weevil), p. 134; 5 *Curculio nucum* L. (Nut
Weevil), p. 138; 6 *Rhynchaenus salicis* L., p. 140; 7 *Byctiscus populi* L.
(Poplar Leaf Roller), p. 140; 8 *Cionus scrophulariae* L. (Figwort Weevil),
p. 138; 9 *Attelabus nitens* Scop., p. 140.

or example. To the layman the meadow appears to have a fairly uniform surface covered with various kinds of grasses and flowering plants. To the Beetle collector, however, it consists of a number of different habitats. The composition of the Beetle fauna will vary according to the condition of the ground; whether it is wet or dry, or densely overgrown, and whether it is in the sun or overshadowed by a hedge. The Beetles found on the banks of a stream and on the water plants will be quite different to those found in the grassy parts. The aspect of the site, whether it faces north, south, east or west, the nature of the surrounding land, whether it is sheltered by deciduous or coniferous trees, the type and regularity of manuring, and last but not least, the time of the year, all influence the Beetle fauna. In spring when the ground is wet, the most common species are those associated with a damp habitat, but when the hay has been cut and the ground dries out, these will give place to species associated with a dry habitat.

Weather conditions are also very important. Beetles are very active before a storm, but some hours before the downpour they will seek shelter beneath leaves and stones. The Cantharidae, especially *Rhagonycha fulva* (Soldier Beetle), take up a characteristic position—they hang upside-down under a leaf. The Southern European species of Cebrionids behave in the same way. An experienced observer can accurately forecast a storm by watching these insects.

It need hardly be mentioned that the composition of the Beetle fauna varies greatly with the season of the year, as many species have only a short adult life.

In early spring the most profitable collecting is in sunny, sheltered places. Here small Ground Beetles and Rove Beetles will be found. The Ladybirds are some of the earliest species to appear, being enticed by the sun from their winter quarters in cracks and crevices.

43

Finally we give a short list of habitats, and the Beetles associated with them.

Marshy river banks: Heteroceridae, Hydrophilidae, *Bembidion*, *Stenus*, *Chlaenius*.

Shingle-beds: Carabidae, Staphylinidae.

Under stones, in moss and under decaying vegetation: Carabidae, Staphylinidae, Pselaphidae, Scydmaenidae, Clavicornia and many other Beetles which have sought shelter from the rain.

Under bark: Clavicornia, Staphylinidae, Histeridae, Ipidae, Cerambycidae, Carabidae.

In dead and decaying wood and mossy stumps, especially those of deciduous trees: Scaphidiidae, Ciidae, Erotylidae, Endomychidae, Tenebrionidae and Alleculidae.

In fungi: Staphylinidae.

In Puff-balls: Endomychidae and *Pocadius*.

In carrion: Silphidae, Staphylinidae, Histeridae.

In dry carrion and on bones: Necrobia, Nitidula, Dermestes, Trox.

In dung: coprophagous Scarabidae (Dung Beetles), Hydrophilidae, Staphylinidae, Histeridae.

On warm sandy banks: Carabidae, large Staphylinid species, Byrrhidae, Tenebrionidae, Curculionidae, Cicindelidae.

On wood in the sunshine (standing and felled timber): Buprestidae, Cerambycidae, Cleridae, Ipidae.

On flowers of low-growing plants: Phalacridae, Mordellidae, *Anthaxia*, Malacoderms, Cerambycidae.

On the flowers of larger plants: Cerambycidae, Cantharidae, *Hoplia*, *Cetonia*, *Trichius*.

On flowering shrubs: Byturidae, *Anthrenus*, Mordellidae, Nitidulidae, Cerambycidae, Staphylinidae, Alleculidae, *Cetonia*.

On sap flowing from the wounds of trees: Nitidulidae, Lucanidae, *Osmoderma*, Staphylinidae.

44

The Chrysomelidae and Curculionidae are mainly mono-phagous, that is, they feed on one kind of plant; these are chiefly Cruciferae (Shepherd's Purse and its allies), Scro-phulariaceae (Figwort and its allies) and Solanaceae (Potato, Nightshade and their allies). Poplars, oaks, willows and beeches are the food of many Beetles. Indigenous species very rarely attack acclimatized foreign plants.

COLLECTING EQUIPMENT AND THE
PREPARATION OF A COLLECTION

THE EQUIPMENT of the Beetle collector need not be extensive or elaborate. First comes the killing bottle. The best type is a wide-necked vessel of thick glass with a well-fitting cork (Fig. v). Some clean sawdust, or strips of paper are placed in the bottom and moistened with a few drops of killing fluid. Ethyl acetate is by far the most satisfactory killing agent, especially if one part of creosote is added to fifty parts of the fluid. It is advisable to have at least two killing bottles of different sizes, and to keep one for large, and the other for small specimens. Two pairs of forceps are essential; a stout pair for large Beetles, and a fine pair for delicate specimens.

There are several different kinds of collecting nets, each used in a different way. The net used for sweeping through the herbage (Fig. w) must be much more strongly constructed than a butterfly net. It should consist of a stout metal frame, which may be jointed for folding, to which the net or bag is attached, either by rings or else sewn directly over the frame. The bag should be made of strong calico or similar material, and should taper slightly towards the base. A bag of 12 inches diameter and 20 inches long will be found satisfactory. This net can also be used for catching beetles on the wing. A beating tray

Sawdust

Fig. v. Killing bottle.

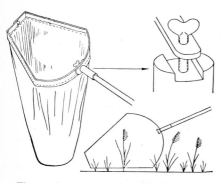

Fig. w. A sweeping net, and the way in which it is used.

(Fig. x) is used to catch the Beetles as they fall when trees and bushes are beaten with a stick.

Many Beetles live in water, especially in algal colonies and on water plants; others live on the plants growing at the water's edge. The mud at the bottom may also harbour a number of interesting species. A water-net (Fig. y) of very strong construction is used for catching these Beetles. The net should be made in the following way: an iron band about $\frac{3}{4}$ inch wide with holes drilled at intervals along its length is bent into a ring or a pentagon. The bag is sewn on with strong twine, using these holes. The sides of the net should be of some strong closely-woven material, whereas the bottom should be of a less dense material so that the water may flow through it more quickly. To catch Hydraenids and Dryopids, the net is firmly anchored, in a place where the stream is narrow and the current swift, in such a way that all the water flows through it. One then stands a little way up-stream and turns over the stones and stirs up the bottom with a stick. After a while the contents of the net are turned out into a shallow white dish and carefully examined.

A sieve is a very useful addition to the collecting equipment. Moss, decaying vegetation and other debris

Fig. x. Beating tray.

is placed in the sieve, which is then shaken over a sheet: insects will fall through and can be picked up with forceps. The specially constructed sieve illustrated in Fig. z is especially useful. It has collapsible canvas sides and a bag attached beneath, into which the siftings fall. The sifted refuse can be taken home in small bags and examined more carefully than is possible in the field. When the debris has been carefully examined two or three times, it should be covered with a damp cloth and

Fig. Y. Pentagonal water-net (part of the side cut away to show the bottom).

put aside in a covered vessel for a few days. A number of insects which have been overlooked will collect in the cloth.

What is to be done with the insects when they have been caught and killed? First, it is wise to leave the insects exposed to the ethyl acetate vapour for at least a day, as this relaxes the specimens and makes them easy to set. The creosote will prevent the formation of moulds and will allow the insect to be stored for a long time, even in a damp condition.

Large Beetles (about 1 cm. long and over) are pinned through the body, using stainless-steel entomological pins of a suitable size. The pin should pass through the right elytron about one-third of the distance from the base. The specimen is pushed up the pin to within $\frac{1}{4}$ inch of its head. Small Beetles should be mounted on oblong or triangular

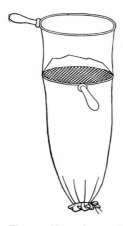

Fig. z. Sieve (part of the side cut away to show the sieve).

mounts of white card (Bristol Board No. 6), using a suitable type of gum, such as gum tragacanth. Triangular mounts are the best as they allow one to examine the underside of the Beetle without any difficulty.

The specimens are set in the following way. When the Beetle is relaxed, a pin is pushed a little way through the body and into a slab of paper-covered cork, so that the Beetle's legs are resting lightly on the surface of the cork. The legs and antennae are extended—using a fine paintbrush or needles mounted in holders, and held in place with pins, one on either side of each appendage. The specimens are then put aside for a few days to dry, taking care to protect them from dust.

A locality label must be placed beside each set Beetle. This should give the name of the locality and the nearest town, together with the date of capture and the name of the collector. A note on the actual habitat may also be added. A correctly made out locality label will look like this:

Shelford, Cambridge.
J. Hunter. 5.7.54.
under stone.

The locality label should be as small as possible, but it must give all the information required. Abbreviations may be used, but not to such an extent that they are incomprehensible to anyone but the owner of the collection. The locality label is placed on the pin below the Beetle.

When the Beetle has been named, a determination label is placed on the pin below the locality label. The determination label should give the name of the genus and species to which the specimen belongs, together with the author's name (or standard abbreviation), followed by the name

49

of the person responsible for the determination and the date, thus:

Chrysolina
staphylea L.
det. Heller 1952.

Det.=determinavit, determined by.

The specimens should be stored in cork-lined boxes, which must have close-fitting lids to prevent the entry of pests, such as the Museum Beetle (*Anthrenus museorum* L.), moths, mites, etc. Each box must be supplied with a suitable disinfectant, such as paradichlorbenzene or naphthalene. DDT is of no use, as the larvae of the Museum Beetle are immune to it.

Under dry, dark conditions the specimens will keep indefinitely. They should not be exposed to direct sunlight as this will cause the colours to fade.

PROTECTED BEETLES

Coleopterists intending to collect on the Continent should note that in Germany a number of Beetles are protected by law: these are: *Lucanus cervus* (Stag Beetle), *Rosalia alpina*, *Calosoma sycophanta* and *Hydrous piceus* (Great Silver Water Beetle). In addition, those interested in Ant's Nest Beetles must not forget that the Red Wood Ant (*Formica rufa*) is also protected. (Special permission is required for the collection of the eggs and larvae for use as fish-food.)

HOW TO USE THE KEYS

T HE KEYS IN THIS BOOK are of the Dichotomous type.
They consist of a number of contrasted descriptions
known as couplets. To use the key one must decide which
description in each couplet, beginning with No. 1, applies
to the Beetle to be named. For instance, the first couplet
reads: First abdominal sternite completely divided by the
hind coxae; or alternatively, First abdominal sternite not
completely divided by the hind coxae. On the right-hand
side, opposite each half of the couplet is a figure indicating
which couplet should be considered next. By working through
the key in this way one will eventually arrive at the generic
and specific name of the Beetle.

In order to distinguish between suborders, families, genera
and so on, a consistent style of printing has been adopted
in the key, which is as follows:

Suborders in capitals—ADEPHAGA

Groups of Families in italic capitals—*PALPICORNIA*

Families in capitals and small capitals—GYRINIDAE

Subfamilies in spaced out small capitals—H A R P A L I N A E

Genera in upper- and lower-case italics—*Harpalus*

Species in lower case italics—*aeneus*

51

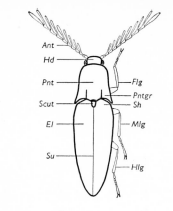

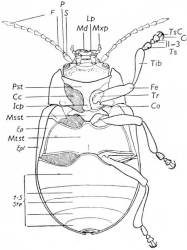

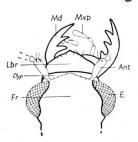

Ant	Antenna	*Md*	Mandible
Cc	Coxal cavity	*Mlg*	Middle leg
Cl	Claw	*Msst*	Mesosternum
Clyp	Clypeus	*Mtst*	Metasternum
Co	Coxa	*Mxp*	Maxillary palp
E	Eye	*P*	Pedicel
El	Elytron	*Pnt*	Pronotum
Ep	Episternum	*Pntgr*	Pronotal groove
Epl	Epipleuron	*Pst*	Prosternum
F	Flagellum	*S*	Scape
Fe	Femur	*Scut*	Scutellum
Flg	Front leg	*Sh*	Shoulder
Fr	Frons	*Ste*	Sternite
Hd	Head	*Su*	Suture
Hlg	Hind leg	*Tib*	Tibia
Icp	Intercoxal	*Tr*	Trochanter
	process	*Ts*	Tarsal segment
Lp	Labial palp	*TsC*	Last tarsal
Lbr	Labrum		segment

Abbreviations used in the text:

abd.	abdomen (see fig. G, p. 13).
ant.	antennae.
el.	elytra.
hd.	head.
pnt.	pronotum.
pthx.	prothorax.
pyg.	pygidium (see fig. G, p. 13).
seg.	segment.
♂	male.
♀	female.
±	more or less.
*	Indicates genera and species not occurring in the British Isles.

52

1. 1st abd. sternite completely divided by the hind coxae, so that its sides are separated from the usually very small median part. First 3 abd. segs. immovably united. All tarsi 5-segmented.   Suborder ADEPHAGA, below
— 1st abd. sternite not completely divided by the hind coxae, visible for its entire breadth behind the coxae. If the coxae are enlarged, then the first 3 abd. sternites are not immovably united. First 3 abd. segs. always separated by distinct sutures.

Suborder POLYPHAGA, page 69

ADEPHAGA

1. 1 pair of eyes present. Front legs longer than middle or hind legs.   2
— 2 pairs of eyes present. Front legs much longer than middle or hind legs.   GYRINIDAE (Whirligig Beetles)

Only 11 species of this family occur in the British Isles. The Beetles move about actively on the surface of the water. *Gyrinus marinus* Gyllh. Fig. 41, p. 71. 5–7 mm. Glabrous; shining blue-black. On standing water. The most widely distributed species in the British Isles. *Orectochilus villosus* Müll. Fig. 42, p. 71. $\pm$ 6 mm. Upperside pubescent; black with a leaden reflection; strongly convex. On running water by night, hiding at grass roots and under stones by day.

2. Terrestrial Beetles, apical ant. segs. clothed with thick fine pubescence.   CARABIDAE (Ground Beetles)
— Aquatic Beetles, apical ant. segs. glabrous.   3
3. Ant. 10-segmented.   HALIPLIDAE

Small elongate-oval Water Beetles, with a coarsely sculptured upperside. Upperside yellow or yellow-brown, with or without black markings. *Haliplus ruficollis* Deg.

Fig. 35, p. 71. 2–2·5 mm. In ponds, usually near the bank.

— Ant. 11-segmented.

DYTISCIDAE (True Water Beetles), page 69

CARABIDAE (Ground Beetles)

The Carabidae are now divided into a large number of families, but in this book they are divided into sub-families. There are about 500 European species, of which over 400 occur in the British Isles. The Carabidae are mainly terrestrial and predacious in habit. They are distinguished by their general shape (with the exception of *Omophron limbatum* F. Colour Plate I, fac. p. 3; found on sandy banks of streams), 11-segmented filiform ant. inserted on the upper surface of the head, and 5-segmented tarsi.

1. Anterior tarsi simple, without a notch on the inner margin. 2
— Anterior tarsi with a notch on the inner margin.

HARPALINAE 5

2. Legs very slender. Mandibles white, long and narrow, with large teeth on the inner surface. Without a strong smell. CICINDELINAE (Tiger Beetles)

Fairly large, active, metallic Beetles. They are often found in large numbers in warm sandy places; they will quickly take to the wing if disturbed. *Cicindela germanica* L. Fig. 2, p. 55, 8–12 mm. The smallest British species. *C. campestris*. Colour Plate I, fac. p. 3, 12–15 mm. El. with isolated small spots. *C. hybrida* L. 12–16 mm. Brownish or greenish-bronze, with a purple reflection; pthx. scarcely narrowed towards the base. Chiefly on coastal sandhills in Britain: also in inland stony places in

Figs. 1–3: 1 *Cicindela silvicola* Dej., p. 56; 2 *C. germanica* L., p. 54; 3 *Calosoma inquisitor* L., p. 56.

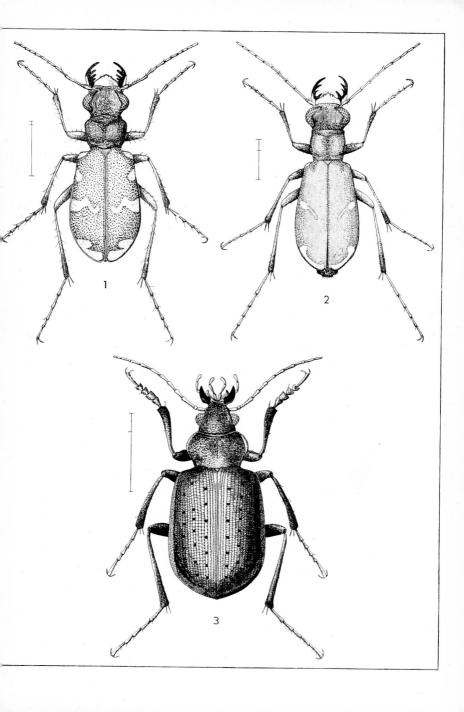

Europe. *C. silvatica* L. 15–17 mm. Ground colour almost black. In sandy places. **C. silvicola* Dej. Fig. 1, p. 55. 14–15 mm. Green with a bronze reflection; el. with zigzag bands. Chiefly in woods.

— Legs stouter. Mandibles dark, short and thick, teeth small or absent. Often with a strong unpleasant odour.

CARABINAE 3

3. Both spines of anterior tibiae apical.   4
— Only one spine of anterior tibiae apical, the other lying on the posterior margin behind the apex.

1. *Notiophilus* Dum. Flat shining Beetles, with large prominent eyes. 2nd el. interval very wide. *N. biguttatus* F. Fig. 12, p. 61. 5–5·5 mm. Upperside coppery; el. with yellow apical patches. Chiefly in woods.
2. *Elaphrus* F. less than 10 mm. long, and *Blethisa* Bon., 11–12 mm. long. Both genera are characterized by large depressions on the el. In marshy places and at the water's edge. Beetles of both genera are able to swim. These two genera form an intermediate group between the Carabinae and the Harpalinae. *Elaphrus riparius* L. Colour Plate I, fac. p. 3. The commonest species.

4. Base of el. not margined. Our largest Ground Beetles belong here.

1. *Calosoma* Web. Hd. short; el. $\pm$ quadrate. *C. sycophanta* L. Colour Plate I, fac. p. 3. 24–30 mm. El. bright metallic green; pthx. margin entire. Rare in the British Isles. *C. inquisitor* L. Fig. 3, p. 55. 16–21 mm. Bronze-brown; sides of pthx. not margined in front of the hind angles. Both species are found on oaks. They feed on caterpillars, and in Europe are especially useful in keeping down the numbers of the Processionary Caterpillars, which do a great deal of damage. **C. maderae*

Figs. 4–6: 4 *Carabus intricatus* L., p. 58; 5 **C. auronitens* F., p. 58; 6 *C. granulatus* L., p. 60.

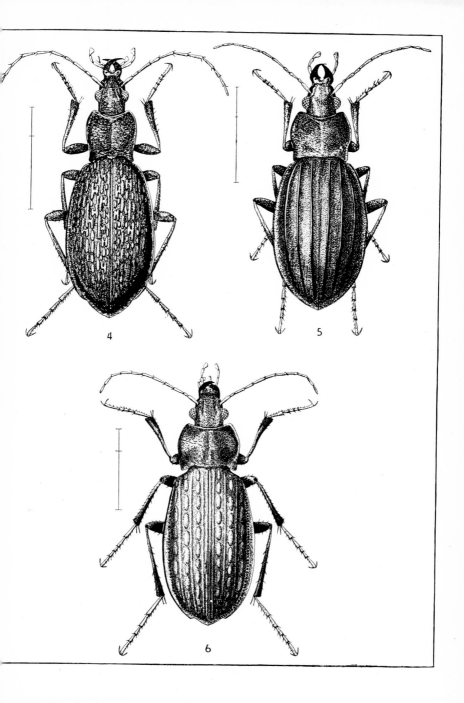

4

5

6

ssp. *auropunctatum* Hbst. 22–30 mm. El. bronze-brown with longitudinal rows of shining golden depressions. In fields and gardens.

2. *Carabus* L. Hd. short; el. regularly oval. Species secreting a malodorous corrosive fluid. El. of ♀ often with an angular emargination before the apex. Anterior tarsi of ♂ expanded.

(a) El. very strongly rugose, with a leathery appearance. *C. coriaceus* L. 34–40 mm. Black. In woods. *C. intricatus* L. Fig. 4, p. 57. 20–27 mm. Blue or violet. In woods.

(b) Upperside bright metallic gold or green. El. with distinct longitudinal ridges. *C. auratus* L. 20–27 mm. El. gold-green, lateral margins red. Rare in the British Isles, but common in many places on the Continent. *C. nitens* L. 14–16 mm. Very similar to Fig. 5, p. 57. Hd., pthx. and margins of el. coppery, el. metallic green, with the ridges blackish. In marshy places. *C. auronitens* F. Fig. 5, p. 57. 18–26 mm. Flatter than *C. auratus* L. El. unicolorous gold-green.

(c) El. smooth and matt, or very finely rugose. Upperside dark-coloured. *C. violaceus* L. (Violet Ground Beetle). 18–32 mm. Dull blue-black, el. margins metallic blue or violet. Under moss and stones. *C. glabratus* Payk. 22–32 mm. Similar to the preceding species but more convex, and the el. without a metallic margin. Chiefly in mountainous regions in the British Isles.

(d) El. regularly and finely striate, with longitudinal rows of shallow round punctures. *C. nemoralis* Müll. 20–26 mm. El. striae not very distinct, punctures dark; upperside blue-black,

Figs. 7–9: 7 *Carabus monilis* F., p. 60; 8 *C. hortensis* L., p. 60; 9 *Cychrus attenuatus* F., p. 60.

58

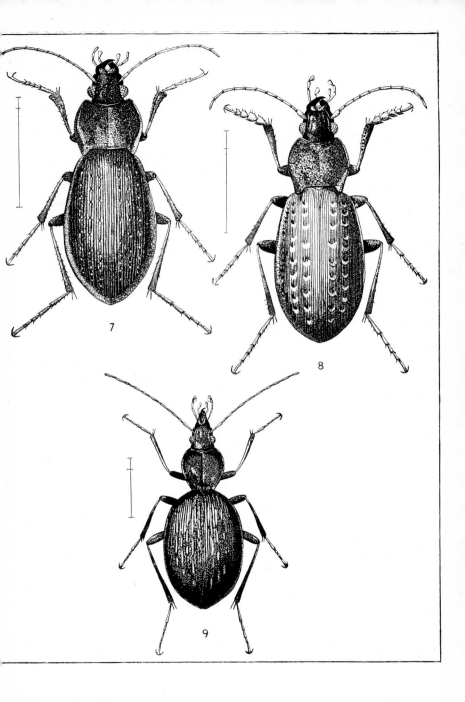

7

8

9

violet or brown. *C. *silvestris* Panz. 19–27 mm. Bright metallic green to coppery. In mountainous regions. *C. *hortensis* L. Fig. 8, p. 59. 23–28 mm. Dark brown, el. depressions gold; el. striae very distinct. In woods.

(e) El. with 3 fine rows of raised oblong granules separated by several raised lines. Coloration metallic, very variable, legs always dark. In fields and at the edges of woods.
C. *monilis* F. Fig. 7, p. 59. 27–30 mm. Granule rows distinct, visible without a lens. Under stones. *C. *scheidleri* Panz. E. Germany and Austria. This species is often regarded as a subspecies of C. *monilis* F.

(f) Raised granules very large, separated by a single well-defined ridge. Upperside bronze, legs often partly red. Under stones.
C. *granulatus* F. Fig. 6, p. 57. 16–22 mm. Body flat.
C. *cancellatus* Illig. 18–26 mm. Body convex.

3. *Cychrus* F. Front of hd. elongate, snout-like; mandibles enlarged. C. *rostratus* L. 15–18 mm. Deep black; very similar to the following species. In woods in mountainous regions. *C. *attenuatus* F. Fig. 9, p. 59. 13–16 mm. El. bronze-brown.

— Base of el. margined; smaller species.

1. *Leistus* Fröl. Hd. with thorn-like prolongation. L. *ferrugineus* L. Fig. 10, p. 61. ± 7 mm. Unicolorous red-brown. In damp, shady places.
2. *Nebria* Latr. Hd. without thorn-like prolongation. N. *brevicollis* F. Fig. 11, p. 61. 9–14 mm. Black; slightly convex. In damp places.

Figs. 10–13: 10 *Leistus ferrugineus* L., p. 60; 11 *Nebria brevicollis* F., p. 60; 12 *Notiophilus biguttatus* F., p. 56; 13 *Clivina fossor* L., p. 62.

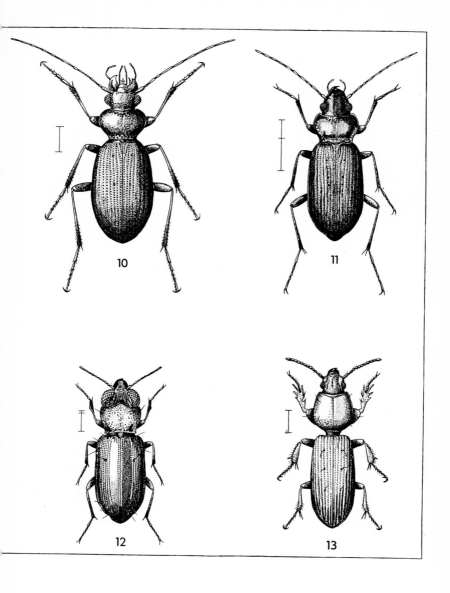

5. El. long, covering entire abd. or only leaving the pyg. exposed.   6
— El. shortened leaving the last few abd. segs. exposed.   14
6. Abd. pedunculate, that is, the body is much constricted between the pthx. and el.   7
— Abd. not pedunculate.   8
7. Anterior tibiae with finger-like projections. Small, narrow, cylindrical Beetles living in burrows or galleries in muddy river banks.

> *Clivina fossor* L. Fig. 13, p. 61. $\pm$ 6 mm. Dark brown without a metallic reflection. *Dyschirius* Bon. Numerous shining metallic species. They burrow in sandy places, or at the edges of streams and ponds.

— Anterior tibiae simple. Larger species.

> *Broscus cephalotes* L. Fig. 14, p. 63. 17–22 mm. Black, matt. In sandy places. This species feigns death when disturbed.

8. Body small, rarely more than 5 mm. long. Anterior tarsi of ♂ with 2 expanded triangular or heart-shaped segs.

> *Bembidion* Latr. Numerous small black species often with a metallic reflection; some species have coloured markings on the el. Ripicoles. *B. ustulatum* L. Colour Plate I, fac. p. 3. 5 mm. *Trechus quadristriatus* Schr. Fig. 16, p. 63. 4 mm. Brown to dark brown. Under moss and stones. **Tachyta nana* Gyllh. Fig. 15, p. 63. Entirely black. Under bark.

— Body much larger. Structure of anterior tarsi different.   9
9. Anterior tarsi of ♂ with 2 or 3 expanded, quadrate or rounded, segments. Upperside nearly always pubescent.

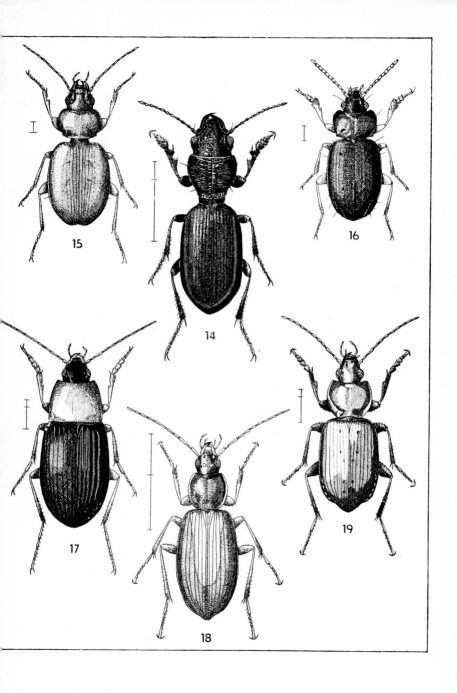

Species smelling strongly of creosote. Under stones in damp and swampy places.

> *Panagaeus crux-major* L. Colour Plate I, fac. p. 3. 7–9 mm. Black with yellow markings on the el.; pubescence erect. *Callistus lunatus* F. 6–7 mm. Pnt. orange, el. yellow with 3 black marks on each; pubescence silky, decumbent. *Chlaenius vestitus* Payk. Colour Plate I, fac. p. 3. 8–11 mm. Pubescence fine and decumbent.

— Anterior tarsi of ♂ with 1 or more segs. heart-shaped or emarginate in front. Body rarely pubescent.   10

10. Anterior tarsi of ♂ with 3 expanded segs.   11

— Anterior tarsi of ♂ with 4 expanded segs.

> 1. *Harpalus* Latr. Body larger, unicolorous. *H. aeneus* F. (=*affinis* Schr.). Fig. 24, p. 65. 9–12 mm. Upper surface glabrous; metallic green, blue, purple or black; legs red or pitchy. *H. rufipes* Deg. (Strawberry Seed Beetle). Fig. 23, p. 65. 14–16 mm. Black; el. clothed with thick, decumbent yellow pubescence. In dry places.
>
> 2. *Acupalpus* Latr. Small species, usually with coloured markings on the el. *A. meridianus* L. Fig. 25, p. 65. 3·5–4 mm. Dark brown with yellow markings. In damp places.

11. Anterior tibiae with 1 apical spine. Chiefly under stones.   12

— Anterior tibiae with 2 apical spines.

> *Zabrus tenebroides* Goeze. Fig. 22, p. 65. 14–16 mm. Pitchy-brown, occasionally with a slight metallic reflection. In corn-fields; the adult insect may do considerable damage by climbing the corn-stalks and feeding on the grain.

Figs. 20–28: 20 *Molops piceus Panz., p. 68; 21 *Amara aenea* Deg., p. 66; 22 *Zabrus tenebriodes* Goeze, p. 64; 23 *Harpalus rufipes* Deg. (Strawberry Seed Beetle), p. 64; 24 *H. aeneus* F., p. 64; 25 *Acupalpus meridianus* L., p. 64; 26 *Lebia cyanocephala* L., p. 68; 27 *Dromius agilis* F., p. 68; 28 **Brachinus explodens* Duft. (Bombardier Beetle), p. 68.

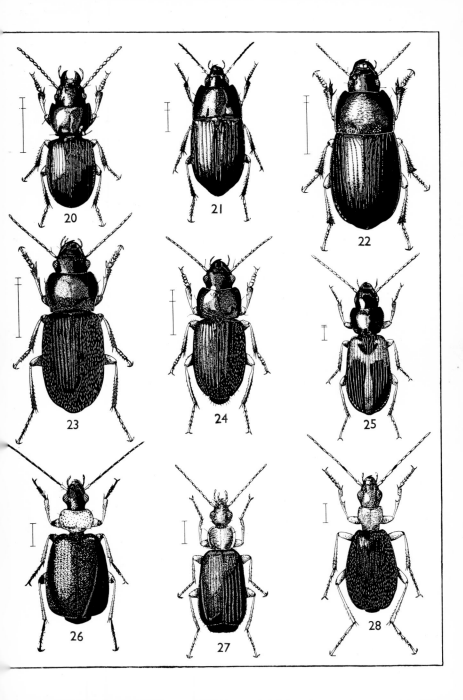

12. Penultimate segment of labial palpi with only 2 setae. (Examine the beetle from the side.) 13
— Penultimate segment of labial palpi with more than 2 setae.

> *Amara* Bon. Numerous, often metallic species, usually found in dry places. *A. aenea* Deg. Fig. 21, p. 65. 6–8 mm. Upperside brassy, greenish, bluish or almost black, base of ant. reddish.

13. Hind trochanters of normal length, ± 1/3 length of femora.

> 1. Claws pectinate or toothed. Body smaller, oval: *Calathus* Bon. *C. melanocephalus* L. Fig. 17, p. 63. 6–8 mm. Black, pthx. red. Body larger, elongate: **Dolichus halensis* Schall. Fig. 18, p. 63. 15–20 mm. Black, legs and ant. yellow, el. often with a red triangular mark behind the scutellum. In fields and on paths.
> 2. Claws simple. Upperside flat: *Agonum* Bon. *A. (Platynus) assimile* Payk. Fig. 29, p. 67. 10–13 mm. Entirely deep black. *A. sexpunctatum* L. Fig. 19, p. 63. 7–9 mm. Bright metallic green to coppery. In damp places and on river banks.

— Hind trochanters much enlarged, almost attaining 1/2 length of femora.

> 1. *Pterostichus* Bon. First 3 ant. segs. glabrous. 3rd el. interval with shallow round pores. *P. cupreus* L. Fig. 30, p. 67. 10–14 mm. Coloration very variable, metallic green, coppery or nearly black; el. striate. In dry fields and on the edges of paths. *P. oblongopunctatus* F. Fig. 31, p. 67. 9–12 mm. Black with a metallic reflection. 3rd el. interval with 4–6 large punctures. In woods. *P. madidus* L.

Figs. 29–34: 29 *Agonum assimile* Payk., p. 66; 30 *Pterostichus cupreus* L., p. 66; 31 *P. oblongopunctatus* F. p. 66; 32 *P. melanarius* Illig., p. 68; 33 **P. burmeisteri* Heer., p. 68; 34 *Abax parallelopipedus* Pill. et Mitt., p. 68.

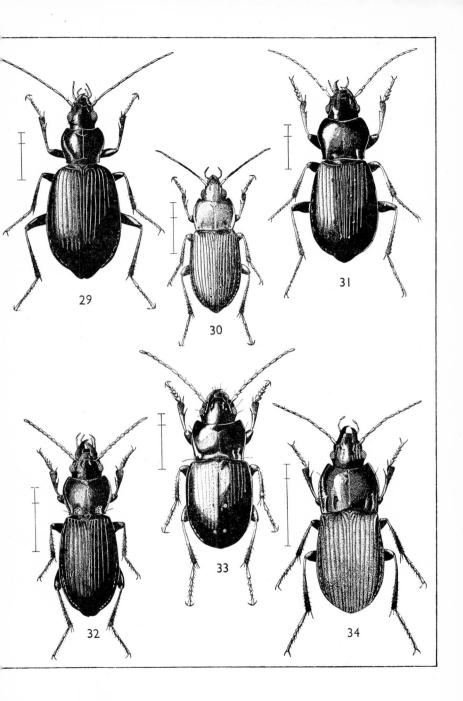

29

30

31

32

33

34

(Black Garden Beetle). Shining black, legs black to reddish. 3rd el. interval with 2 pores behind the middle. *P. burmeisteri* Heer. Fig. 33, p. 67. 12–14 mm. Broad; strongly shining, black, upperside coppery with a purple reflection. El. not striate. In woods in mountainous regions. *P. melanarius* Illig. Fig. 32, p. 67. 13–17 mm. Deep black; el. strie deep.

2. *Abax* Sam. First 3 ant. segs. glabrous. El. intervals without punctures. In woods. *A. parallelopipedus* Pill. et Mitt. Fig. 34, p. 67. 18–25 mm. Entirely black; el. of ♀ less shining.

3. *Molops* Bon. First 2 ant. segs. glabrous. *M. piceus* Panz. Fig. 20, p. 65. Dark brown, underside and legs lighter. In woods under stones and moss.

14. Abd. 6-segmented. Species unable to eject a volatile fluid from the terminal abd. seg.

1. *Lebia* Latr. Base of pthx. drawn out in the middle. *L. cyanocephala* L. Fig. 26, p. 65. ± 6 mm. Metallic green, pthx. yellow. The beetles hunt Plant-lice on the roots and branches of trees and shrubs.

2. *Dromius* Bon. Base of pthx. straight. *D. agilis* F. Fig. 27, p. 65. ± 6 mm. Under bark.

— Abd. 7 (♀) or 8 (♂) segmented. Bombardier Beetles, capable of ejecting a jet of volatile caustic liquid from the terminal abd. seg.; this action is accompanied by a distinctly audible explosive sound.

Brachinus crepitans L. (Bombardier Beetle). 6·5–10 mm. Blue or green, ant. legs and pthx. red. Under stones in sunny places. Very similar in shape to the following species. *B. explodens* Duft. Fig. 28, p. 65. 5 mm.

Aptinus bombarda Illig. Up to 15 mm. long. Black, legs yellow. In woods.

DYTISCIDAE (True Water Beetles)

Predacious insects, living in still and running water. There are about 100 European species most of which also occur in the British Isles.

1. Small species, not more than 5 mm. long.

> *Oreodytes* (=*Deronectes*) *halensis* F. Fig. 36, p. 71. 4–4·5 mm. Black, upperside yellow with black markings. (Lincs. and East Anglia.)

— Larger species, much more than 5 mm. long.   2

2. Eyes emarginate in front, behind the ant. insertions.

> *Agabus bipustulatus* L. Fig. 37, p. 71. 10–11 mm. Brown, rather matt. *Platambus maculatus* L. Fig. 38, p. 71. 7–8 mm. Black, upperside with yellow markings. In running water.

— Eyes not emarginate, but evenly rounded. El. of ♀ often ridged. Anterior tarsi of ♂ with large clasping organs. Coloration dark, lateral margins of pthx. and el. yellow.

> *Acilius sulcatus* L. Fig. 39, p. 71. 16–18 mm. El. with patches of pubescence; dark brown. *Dytiscus marginalis* L. (Great Water Beetle or Diving Beetle). Fig. 40, p. 71. 30–35 mm. Dark olive-green. In large ponds: in this country it is a serious enemy of young fish, both in its adult and larval stages.

POLYPHAGA

(See also Crowson's key on page 142)

1. Ant. very short; usually shorter than the palpi. Species living in water and dung.   *PALPICORNIA*, p. 72

— Ant. longer than the palpi.   2

2. Ant. with apical segs. enlarged on one side to form a

69

lamellate club, which can be opened and closed, or the ant. strongly elbowed and the segs. of the club immovable. *LAMELLICORNIA*, p. 108
— Ant. without such a club. 3
3. Hd. elongate in front of the eyes, forming a rostrum. All tarsi 4-segmented. *RHYNCHOPHORA*, p. 132
— Hd. not elongate in front of the eyes. 4
4. All tarsi 4-segmented. Ant. neither clubbed nor elbowed, usually filiform. *PHYTOPHAGA*, p. 116
— Tarsi not 4-segmented; or if 4-segmented, then the ant. clubbed. 5
5. Tarsal formula 5, 5, 4 (fore, mid and hind tarsi).
HETEROMERA, p. 101
— Tarsal formula not 5, 5, 4; or if 5, 5, 4, then the el. short exposing part of the abd. 6
6. Anterior coxae long, freely movable in all directions. El. truncate exposing strongly chitinized abd. tergites.
STAPHYLINOIDEA, p. 73
— Anterior coxae shorter, usually globular, movable only backwards and forwards: First 3–4 abd. tergites only feebly chitinized. *DIVERSICORNIA*

> As determinations using morphological characters alone present considerable difficulties (the group includes many small and very small species), we have stressed the typical habitat of each group.

1. Small terrestrial species, almost always with short, clubbed antennae.
CLAVICORNIA (+*BRACHYMERA*), p. 90

Figs. 35–43: 35 *Haliplus ruficollis* Deg., p. 53; 36 *Oreodytes halensis* F., p. 69; 37 *Agabus bipustulatus* L., p. 69; 38 *Platambus maculatus* L., p. 69; 39 *Acilius sulcatus* L., p. 69; 40 *Dytiscus marginalis* L. (Great Water Beetle), p. 69; 41 *Gyrinus marinus* Gyllh. (Whirligig Beetle), p. 53; 42 *Orectochilus villosus* Müll., p. 53; 43 *Hydraena riparia* Kugel., p. 72.

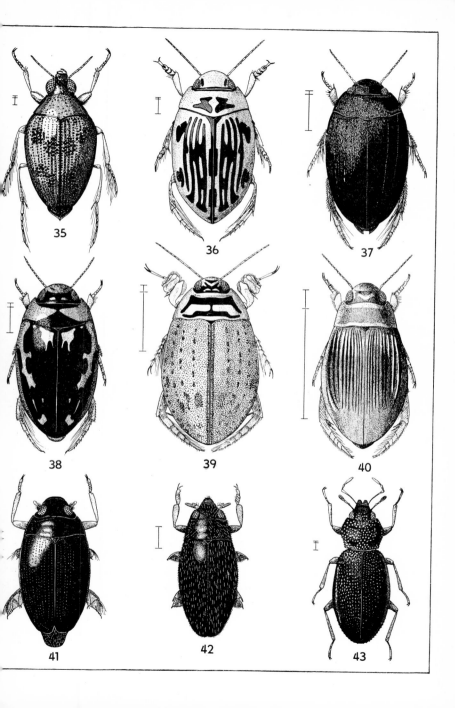

35

36

37

38

39

40

41

42

43

2. Aquatic and bank-inhabiting species.
   HYDROPHILI, p. 90
3. Soft-bodied species, with the upperside usually brightly coloured and pubescent. They live on many different kinds of plants.   *MALACODERMATA*, p. 80
4. Hard-bodied, usually slender species. Intercoxal process of prosternum spine-like.   *STERNOXIA*, p. 84
5. Species living in and on wood. Hd. short. (The Bark Beetles are included in the Rhynchophora as they have elongate heads.)   *TEREDILIA*, p. 100

PALPICORNIA

A single family: HYDROPHILIDAE (Water Beetles)

1. Pnt. without longitudinal furrows or depressions.   3
— Pnt. with longitudinal furrows or depressions.   2
2. Last seg. of hind tarsi shorter than total length of basal segs. Pnt. with 5 longitudinal grooves.

> *Helophorus* L. *H. aquaticus* L. 4–9 mm. Pthx. greenish, el. yellow-brown with black variable markings. On damp banks and in shallow water; often covered with mud.

— Last seg. of hind tarsi longer than the total length of the basal segs. Pnt. with single median longitudinal groove, and lateral longitudinal depressions. Sluggish species living under stones in running water.

> *Hydraena riparia* Kugel. Fig. 43, p. 71. 2·2–4 mm. Black, el. often brownish-black, legs red.

3. Hind tarsi 4- or 5-segmented: if 5-segmented, then seg. 1 shorter than 2. Aquatic species.

> 1. *Berosus* Leach. Easily recognized by the elongate, strongly punctured scutellum. *B. luridus* L. Fig. 44, p. 75. ± 4 mm. Yellow-brown, pnt. with a metallic reflection. In standing water.

2. *Hydrous* Dahl. Distinguished by the large size and characteristic coloration, black with an olive-green reflection. *H. piceus* L. (Great Silver Water Beetle). Fig. 45, p. 75. 34–37 mm. Abd. sternites with median longitudinal ridge. **Hydrous aterimus* Eschsch. 20–30 mm. Abd. sternites without a median longitudinal ridge. In large ponds.

3. *Hydrophilus caraboides* L. Fig. 46, p. 75. 14–18 mm. Similar to *Hydrous piceus*, but it may be distinguished from this species by its smaller size.

4. *Hydrobius fuscipes* L. Fig. 47, p. 75. 6–8 mm. El. deeply striate; black with a brown metallic reflection. In damp ditches.

— Tarsi 5-segmented; 1st seg. of hind tarsus longer than 2nd. Terrestrial Beetles.

1. *Sphaeridium scarabaeoides* L. Fig. 48, p. 75. 5–7 mm. El. confusedly punctate; tibiae with stout spines; black with reddish-yellow markings on the el. In dung.

2. *Coelostoma orbiculare* F. Fig. 49, p. 75. $\pm$ 4 mm. El. confusedly punctate; tibiae with fine spines; body almost semi-spherical. Unicolorous black, rather shining. On muddy banks and in damp places.

3. *Cercyon* Leach. El. punctate-striate. Upperside glabrous. *C. haemorrhoidalis* F. $\pm$ 3 mm. Apex of el. red; base of ant. sometimes red. *C. unipunctatus* L. Fig. 50, p. 75. $\pm$ 3 mm. El. yellow with a median black mark. In dung.

4. *Cryptopleurum* Muls. El. punctate-striate. Upperside pubescent. *C. minutum* F. $\pm$ 2 mm. Black. In dung.

STAPHYLINOIDEA

This large group includes many small and very small species. More than 1000 species occur in the British Isles.

1. Tarsi apparently unsegmented. Wings feather-like. The smallest species (mostly under 1 mm.) belong here.

The Beetles are often found flying in large swarms at sunset. PTILIIDAE

— Tarsi distinctly segmented. Wings normal. 2

2. Palpi elongate with terminal seg. enlarged. 3

— Palpi short. 4

3. El. truncate. PSELAPHIDAE

> 1. Ant. 6-segmented: *Claviger testaceus* Preyssl. (Yellow Ants' Nest Beetle). ± 2 mm. Yellow, shining. In Ants' nests.
>
> 2. Ant. 10- or 11-segmented: *Pselaphus heisei* Hbst. Fig. 56, p. 77. Under 2 mm. long. Yellow-brown. Under decaying vegetation.

— El. not truncate, covering the entire abd.
SCYDMAENIDAE

> *Stenichius collaris* Müll. Under 1·5 mm. long. Black, shining. In moss, decaying vegetation, etc.
> *Euconnus wetterhalli* Grav. 1·5 mm. Black, ant. and legs red. Under decaying vegetation. *E. claviger* Müll. 1·4–1·7 mm. In the nest of the Ant *Lasius brunneus*. *E. fimentarius* Chaud. 1–1·5 mm. Black, legs lighter. Under vegetable refuse.

4. Only 1 or 2 abd. tergites membranous, the remainder, which are usually not covered by the el., are strongly chitinized. STAPHYLINIDAE (Rove Beetles)

> 1. *Anthobium sorbi* Gyllh. Fig. 57, p. 77. 1·5–2 mm. Pale yellow, abd. black (♂) or brown (♀). El. long. In flowers.
>
> 2. *Omalium rivulare* Payk. ± 4 mm. El. structure similar

Figs. 44–51: 44 *Berosus luridus* L., p. 72; 45 *Hydrous piceus* L. (Great Silver Water Beetle), p. 73; 46 *Hydrophilus caraboides* L., p. 73; 47 *Hydrobius fuscipes* L., p. 73; 48 *Sphaeridium scarabaeoides* L., p. 73; 49 *Coelostoma orbiculare* F., p. 73; 50 *Cercyon unipunctatus* L., p. 73; 51 *Catops fuscus* Panz., p. 79.

74

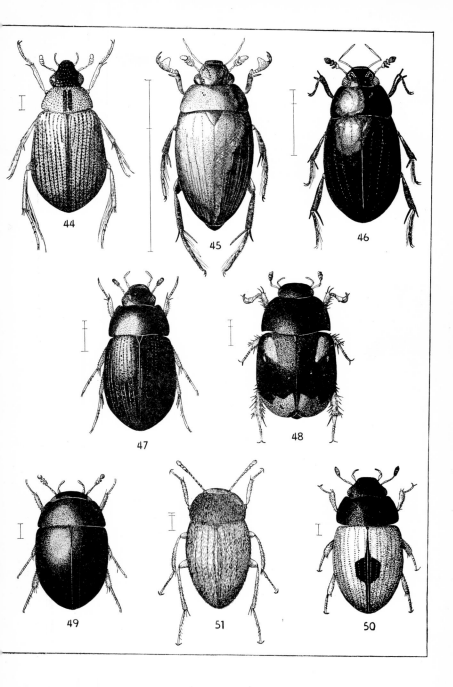

to the preceding species. Dark brown; broad, flat. In fungi and under decaying vegetation. Other species of this genus are found under bark.

3. *Coprophilus striatulus* F. $\pm$ 6 mm. Brownish-black, ant. and legs lighter. Tarsal formula 5, 5, 5. Similar to the following species. In dung.

4. *Oxytelus rugosus* F. Fig. 58, p. 77. 4·5–5 mm. Tarsal formula 3, 3, 3. In dung and refuse. *O. tetracarinatus* Bl. $\pm$ 2 mm. This species is often seen flying in large swarms at sunset. The glandular secretions of the Beetles may cause a burning sensation in the eyes.

5. *Stenus biguttatus* L. Fig. 59, p. 77. 4·5–5 mm. Abd. cylindrical, legs very slender. Blackish-grey with 2 red spots on the el. Numerous *Stenus* species are found on river banks.

6. *Paederus littoralis* Grav. Colour Plate II, fac. p. 10, $\pm$ 8 mm. Easily recognized by its characteristic coloration.

7. *Lathrobium geminum* Kr. 8–9 mm. Black, legs red, el. with base blackish. Easily recognized by its long, narrow, cylindrical shape. In woods under moss and stones.

8. *Philonthus politus* L. $\pm$ 1 mm. Metallic bronze-green. Similar in shape to the following species. Pnt. smooth and glabrous with 2 longitudinal rows of coarse punctures on the disk. Under decaying vegetation.

9. *Staphylinus* L. This genus includes a number of large species with the pnt. clothed with a fine pubescence.

S. caesareus Cederh. Colour Plate II, fac. p. 10. 17–25 mm. Brightly coloured. On the edges of paths. *S. olens* Müll. (Devil's Coach Horse, Cocktail). Dull black, clothed with dark pubescence. Entire upperside finely and closely punctured. When alarmed it assumes a menacing attitude, opening its jaws and erecting its abdomen.

Figs. 52–60: 52 *Necrophorus vespillo* L., p. 79; 53 *Xylodrepa 4-punctata* L., p. 80; 54 *Liodes cinnamomea* Panz., p. 80; 55 *Scaphidium 4-maculatum* Oliv., p. 79; 56 *Pselaphus heisei* Hbst., p. 74; 57 *Anthobium sorbi* Gyllh., p. 74; 58 *Oxytelus rugosus* F., p. 76; 59 *Stenus biguttatus* L., p. 76; 60 *Hister 4-maculatus* L., p. 78.

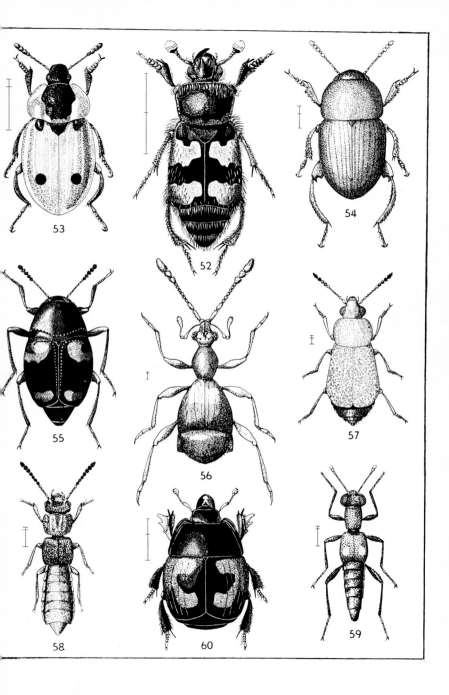

10. *Ontholestes murinus* L. 14–19 mm. Black with a metallic reflection. Entire upperside clothed with a dense grey or yellow mottled pubescence.

11. *Emus hirtus* L. 18–28 mm. Easily recognized by the long thick pubescence. Pubescence black except for the hd. pnt. and the last 3 abd. tergites which are clothed with a thick yellow pubescence. El. with a transverse band of grey pubescence. In and around dung. Very rare in Britain and rare in Europe.

12. *Creophilus maxillosus* L. (Carrion Beetle). 14–22 mm. Black, el. and abd. with scattered patches of greyish-white pubescence. On carcasses and dung.

13. *Bolitobius* (=*Lordithon*) *lunulatus* L. 5–6 mm. Red, el. black with a red transverse mark in front of the middle, and with the posterior margin yellow. Body feebly convex; abd. strongly narrowed towards the apex. In fungi.

14. *Tachyporus chrysomelinus* L. 3·3–5 mm. Very similar in shape to the preceding species. Black, pthx. and el. red, the latter blackish at the base. Ant. slender. Under moss.

— At least the first 3 or 4 abd. tergites membranous; el. longer, body broader.   5

5. Ant. elbowed (scape long)   6
— Ant. not elbowed (scape short)   7
6. Body smaller, broad; upperside flat and very shining; ant. with short compact club; el. striate.   HISTERIDAE

A. Pnt. and el. without longitudinal keels.
1. *Hister* L. Body broad, strongly convex, very shining. In carrion and refuse. *H. quadrimaculatus* L. Fig. 60, p. 77. 7–11 mm. Black, el. with red patches. *H. cadaverinus* Hoffm. 5·5–8 mm. Unicolorous black.
2. *Saprinus semistriatus* Scriba. 3·5–5·5 mm. Black with a metallic reflection. Under decaying vegetation.
3. **Hololepta plana* Sulzer, 8–9 mm. Body very flat; black. Under the bark of poplars.

78

4. *Platysoma compressum* Hbst. 3–3·5 mm. Similar to the preceding species but smaller. Under the bark of oaks and beeches.

B. Pnt. and el. with strongly raised longitudinal keels. *Onthophilus striatus* Forst. 1·8–2 mm. Unicolorous black. Under vegetable refuse.

— Body larger, more than 10 mm. long. Ant. club lamellate.　　　*Necrophorus* (see Silphidae No. 3, p. 79)

7. Body globular or flat, not elongate-oval.　　　　　　　8

— Body elongate-oval, abd. pointed; glabrous, shining species. On fungi and tree fungi.　　　SCAPHIDIIDAE

> *Scaphidium quadrimaculatum* Oliv. Fig. 55, p. 77. 5–6 mm. Black with red markings. Very active Beetles.

8. Globular Beetles able to roll up into a ball. In fungi.
　　　　　　　　　LIODIDAE Subfamily ANISOTOMINAE

> *Anisotoma humeralis* F. 3–4 mm. Globular; very shining black, legs and shoulders of el. red.

— Beetles unable to roll up into a ball, not globular.　　9

9. Tibiae without longitudinal ridges; body small, clothed with fine pubescence. (see Silphidae No. 1 and 2) 10

— Tibiae without longitudinal ridges; body large and pubescent, or small and glabrous.　　　　　　　10

10. Hd. small, not sunk into the pthx., body large usually more than 10 mm. long.　SILPHIDAE (Carrion Beetles)

> 1. *Choleva angustata* F., ± 5 mm. Ant. long, only slightly thickened towards the apex. Dark brown, legs lighter. In damp places and under decaying vegetation.
> 2. *Catops fuscus* Panz. Fig. 51, p. 75. 4–4·5 mm. Ant. distinctly thickened towards the apex. Brownish-black. In dark places and cellars. *C. tristis* Panz. 3·5–4 mm. Similar to the preceding species. On carcasses.
> 3. *Necrophorus* (Sexton or Burying Beetles). Large Beetles with elbowed antennae. On carcasses. *N. germanicus* L. 20–35 mm. Black, ant. club black. *N. vespillo* L. Fig. 52,

p. 77. 11–22 mm. El. with orange markings. *N. humator* F. 18–25 mm. Black, ant. club red.

4. Body flat; el. with longitudinal ridges. *Xylodrepa quadripunctata* L. Fig. 53, p. 77. 12–14 mm. Black, upperside yellow with black markings. In oaks and beeches, preying on caterpillars. *Blitophaga* (=*Aclypea*) *opaca* L. (Beet Carrion Beetle). 9–12 mm. Black, clothed with a golden-brown pubescence. A beet pest. *Oeceoptoma thoracicum* L. 12–16 mm. Black, hd. and pnt. clothed with a bright red pubescence. On carcasses. *Thanatophilus sinuatus* F. 9–12 mm. Black, pubescence black. On carcasses. *Silpha obscura* L. 13–19 mm. Black, upperside glabrous; hd. short. On carcasses and in fields. *Phosphuga atrata* L. Black or dark brown, glabrous; hd. elongate, snout-like. Under bark and in moss.

— Hd. larger, sunk into the pthx. Body small, yellowish, glabrous and shining. In fungi and under fungus-infected bark.   LIODIDAE

    Liodes cinnamomea Panz. Fig. 54, p. 77. 4–6 mm.

MALACODERMATA

1. Scutellum simple, without a longitudinal keel.   2
— Scutellum with a longitudinal keel. Wood-feeding Beetles.   LYMEXYLIDAE

    Hyloecoetes dermestoides L. Fig. 67, p. 83. 6–18 mm. Yellow-brown to dark-brown, el. sometimes black. In woods, especially on and near dead and dying trees.

2. Ant. filiform, without clubbed or thickened apical segs. 3
— Ant. with thickened apical segs.   CLERIDAE

    1. Ant. with thickened apical segs. The larvae are carnivorous and prey on wood-feeding larvae: *Thanasimus formicarius* L. (Ant Beetle). 7–10 mm. Black, underside, scutellum and base of el. red; el. with 2 transverse bands of white pubescence, one before and one behind the

middle. *Korynetes coeruleus* Deg. 3–6 mm. Bright blue, ant. and legs black. About old timber. The larvae of this species prey on the larvae of the Death Watch Beetle. *Trichodes apiarius* L. Colour Plate II, fac. p. 10. On flowers.

2. Ant. with a compact 3 segmented club. On bones and dry carrion: *Necrobia ruficollis* F. Fig. 66, p. 83. 4–6 mm. Red, hd. ant. and abd. black, el. blue with the shoulders red. *N. violacea* L. 4–5 mm. unicolorous green or blue. *N. rufipes* Deg. 3–4 mm. Very like the preceding species but with the legs red.

3. Body small, round or broadly oval. HELODIDAE

Cyphon variabilis Thunb. Fig. 79, p. 89. 2–3 mm. Light brown, pubescent; body oval; hind femora not enlarged. On plants in damp places. *Scirtes hemisphaericus* L. ± 3 mm. Brownish-black, clothed with a dense pubescence. Body almost semi-spherical; hind femora enlarged. (The Beetles are able to jump.) On plants in damp places.

— Body elongate, el. parallel-sided or widening towards the apex.   4

4. Femora and tibiae broad and flat.   5

— Femora and tibiae ± cylindrical.   6

5. El. with regular longitudinal ridges. LYCIDAE

Lygistopterus sanguineus L. Fig. 61, p. 83. 6–12 mm. El. and margins of pthx. red. On flowers in woods. *Dictyopterus aurora* Hbst. 6–9 mm. Similar to the preceding species. Ant., underside and legs black, el. scarlet. Under the bark of spruce fir in Scotland. *D. affinis* Payk. 6–8 mm. Similar to the preceding species but smaller; pthx. black. On bracken.

— El. without regular longitudinal ridges, abd. with luminous organs (yellow patches). ♀ larviform with the el. very much shortened or absent. The ♀, which is unable to fly, is more strongly luminous than the ♂ which is able to fly.

LAMPYRIDAE

Lampyris noctiluca L. ♂ Fig. 62, p. 83. ♂ 11–12 mm. El. grey-brown. ♀ 16–18 mm. Brown; entirely wingless. In grassy places. The ♀ is known as the Glow-worm.
Phausis splendicula L. 8–10 mm. ♂ grey-brown; ♀ yellow-brown, with small scale-like el.

6. Posterior coxae not conical and emergent.

DASCILLIDAE

Dascillus cervinus L. Fig. 78, p. 89. ± 11 mm. ♂ yellow-brown clothed with a yellow pubescence; ♀ black clothed with a grey pubescence. On flowers (chiefly Umbelliferae) and bushes.

— Posterior coxae conical and emergent.   7
7. Labrum not visible.

CANTHARIDAE

1. *Podabrus alpinus* Payk. 11–14 mm. General shape similar to *Cantharis* (see below). Base of pthx. curved; colour very variable. Chiefly on coniferous trees.
2. *Cantharis* L. Base of pthx. straight. Chiefly on bushes. *C. rustica* Fall. Fig. 63, p. 83. 10–15 mm. Front of hd., pnt. (except for a black spot in the middle of the disk), femora and abd. mainly reddish-yellow. *C. fusca* L. 11–15 mm. General shape and coloration similar to the preceding species; legs black. *C. obscura* L. 9–13 mm. Similar to the preceding species but the pnt. black with the sides red. *C. haemorrhoidalis* F. 6·5–10 mm. Yellow, posterior part of hd. and large mark on pnt. black. *C. darwiniana* Shp. 7·5–9·5 mm. Colour variable, yellow-brown to dark brown, anterior margin of pnt. and posterior margin of hd. yellow. Under seaweed.

Figs. 61–67: 61 *Lygistopterus sanguineus* L., p. 81; 62 *Lampyris noctiluca* L. ♂, p. 82; 63 *Cantharis rustica* Fall., p. 82; 64 *Rhagonycha fulva* Scop. (Soldier Beetle), p. 84; 65 *Dasytes plumbeus* Müll., p. 84; 66 *Necrobia ruficollis* F., p. 81; 67 *Hyloecoetes dermestoides* L., p. 80.

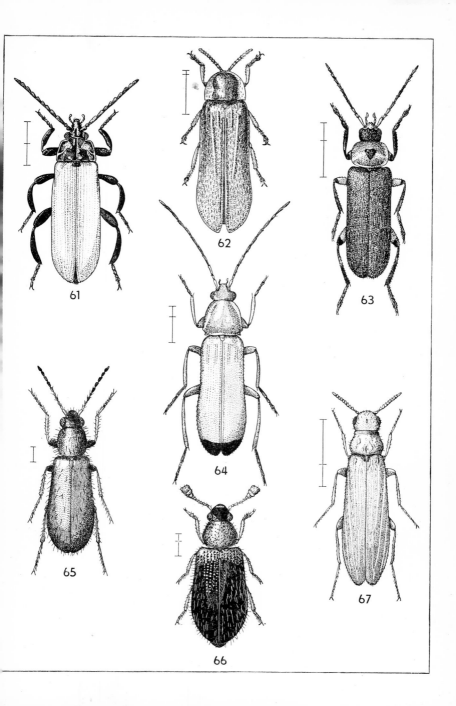

61

62

63

64

65

66

67

3. *Rhagonycha fulva* Scop. (Soldier Beetle). Fig. 64, p. 83.
7–10 mm. Reddish-yellow, apex of el. black. Chiefly on
Umbelliferae.

4. *Malthinus* Latr. Small species with short el. In damp
places.

— Labrum visible from above.
MELYRIDAE (=MALACHIIDAE+DASYTIDAE)

1. Pnt. smooth, not punctate, upperside finely pubescent
(Malachiidae). **Charopus flavipes* Payk. $\pm$ 2·5 mm.
Blackish-green, legs partly yellow. In damp places.
Malachius aeneus L. 6–7 mm. Shorter and stouter than
Cantharis; metallic green, ♂ with sides of pthx and el. red;
♀ similar to ♂ but with el. red, with a triangular metallic
green mark at the base. On flowers.

2. Pnt. strongly punctate, upperside thickly pubescent
(Dasytidae). *Dasytes plumbeus* Müll. Fig. 65, p. 83.
$\pm$ 4 mm. Black with a leaden reflection, pubescence grey,
femora dark, tibia and tarsi lighter brown. On flowering
shrubs. *D. aerosus* Kiesw. 4–4·5 mm. The common
British species is very similar to the preceding species
but has the legs entirely black.

STERNOXIA

1. 1st abd. sternites not separated by well-defined sutures;
pthx. firmly attached to mesothorax, not freely mov-
able.   2

— All abd. sternites separated by well-defined sutures;
pthx. loosely attached to mesothorax, freely movable.
When laid on their backs the Beetles are capable of
leaping into the air and coming down upon their feet.
ELATERIDAE (Click Beetles, Skipjacks)

Over 50 species occur in the British Isles. They are all
very alike and difficult to separate. Some larvae, known
as Wireworms, feed on grass and plant roots and often
cause great damage. Others are predacious.

(a) Prosternum with short deep grooves for the reception of the ant.

Lacon (=Agrypnus) murinus L. Fig. 68, p. 87. 12–17 mm. Body broad; pubescence grey or brown, with white patches. In dry places, under stones and on low-growing plants.

(b) Prosternum without such grooves.

1. Corymbites Latr. (Upland Click Beetles.) Large, often metallic species. Ant. pectinate (♂) or serrate (♀). C. sjoelandicus Müll. 12–15 mm. Black, with a copper or bronze reflection; el. with irregular patches of white pubescence. In damp meadows. C. pectinicornis L. ♂ Fig. 69, p. 87. 15–18 mm. Bright metallic green to copper; upperside closely punctate. C. aeneus L. 10–15 mm. Upperside very shining, metallic blue, green or coppery. Ant. of ♂ not serrate; pnt. almost smooth. Chiefly in pine woods. *C. purpureus Poda. 10–11 mm. Black, el. red, pnt. with thick red pubescence. In woods.

2. Agriotes Eschsch. Non-metallic, distinctly pubescent species. On flowers and on arable land. The larvae are one of the most serious pests of arable land. A. obscurus L. 8–9 mm. Pthx. dark brown, el. lighter or darker brown. The larva is the most common Wireworm pest. A. sputator L. 5–6 mm. Colour very variable, light to dark brown. A. lineatus L. Fig. 70, p. 87. 7–10 mm. Pthx. red-brown to dark brown, el. with alternate dark and light brown longitudinal pubescent lines. A. pallidulus Illig. 3–4 mm. Much narrower than the preceding species; pthx. black, el. yellowish-red with the suture darker.

3. Adrastus nitidulus Marsh. 4–5 mm. Hd. and pthx. shining black, el. yellow-brown with apex and suture darker, ant. and legs yellow. On herbage.

4. Athous Eschsch. Larger pubescent species. In woods, on trees and bushes. *A. niger L. Fig. 71, p. 87. 10–14 mm. Unicolorous black, el. sometimes yellow-brown. A. vittatus F. 9–13 mm. Black or brownish-black, el. dark-brown to reddish-brown, suture often darker. A. haemorrhoidalis F.

(Garden Click Beetle). 9–13 mm. Dark brown, el. sometimes reddish-brown, pubescence grey.

5. *Melanotus rufipes* Hbst. 10–18 mm. Dark brownish-
black, legs reddish-yellow. Claws pectinate. In decaying
wood.

6. *Elater balteatus* L. 7–9 mm. Black, el. red, with the
apical 1/3 black. In the stumps of fir trees. *E. sanguino-
lentus* Schr. 9–11 mm. Black, el. red with a variable black
sutural mark.

2. Ant. clubbed; small species.   TRIXAGIDAE

Trixagus dermestoides L. Fig. 73, p. 87. ± 3 mm. Grey,
clothed with a dense grey pubescence. In grass, especially
in woods.

— Ant. serrate, not clubbed.   3
3. Tibiae cylindrical, not flattened.

                         BUPRESTIDAE (Jewel Beetles)

There are over 300 species of this family in Europe,
but only 12 occur in the British Isles, and some of these
are very rare.

1. Large species; body broad, feebly convex. On wood
in the sunshine.

*Chalcophora mariana L. Fig. 74, p. 89. 24–30 mm.
Shining coppery-bronze, underside bright coppery.
Upperside with irregular longitudinal furrows filled with
coarse sculpture and patches of thick white pubescence.
In pine woods.

*Dicera berolinensis Hbst. Fig. 75, p. 89. 20–24 mm.
Shining coppery, el. with longitudinal rows of darker
patches. In beech woods. **Lampra rutilans* F. Colour
Plate II, fac. p. 10. 12–15 mm. Shining metallic green on
golden-green. On lime trees. **Buprestis rustica* L. Colour

Figs. 68–73: 68 *Lacon murinus* L., p. 85; 69 *Corymbites pectinicornis* L.,
p. 85; 70 *Agriotes lineatus* L., p. 85; 71 **Athous niger* L., p. 85; 72 *Melasis
buprestoides* L., p. 88; 73 *Trixagus dermestoides* L., p. 86.

86

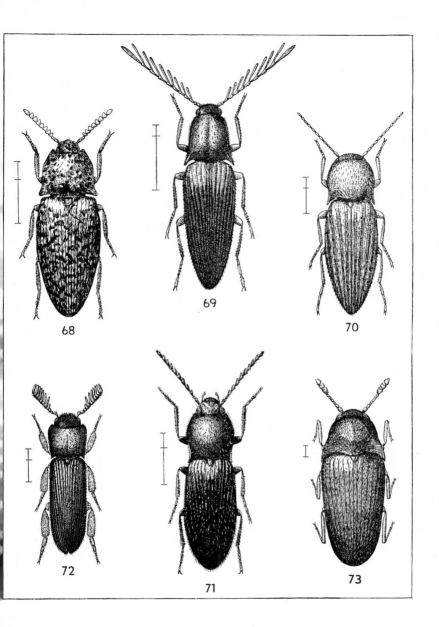

68

69

70

72

71

73

Plate II, fac. p. 10, 12–18 mm. Coloration metallic. *B. octoguttata L. Colour Plate II, fac. p. 10. 10–15 mm. Metallic blue with yellow markings. In pine woods. *Chrysobothris affinis F. Fig. 76, p. 89. 12–14 mm. Dark coppery, el. with golden depressions. On tree trunks.

2. Smaller species, usually less than 10 mm. long; body broad and flat. Chiefly in woods, on flowers and tree trunks.

Anthaxia nitidula L. Colour Plate II, fac. p. 10. 5–7 mm. Pnt. with lateral depressions. ♂ and ♀ differently coloured. On flowers; very rare in the British Isles. *A. fulgurans F. Colour Plate II, fac. p. 10. 5–6 mm. Pnt. without lateral depressions. *A. submontana Obenb. ± 6 mm. Unicolorous dark brown.

3. Body cylindrical, very elongate. On trees and on flowers.

Agrilus biguttatus F. Colour Plate II, fac. p. 10. ± 10 mm. Metallic, el. with 2 patches of white pubescence. On bushes and oak trees. A. viridis L. 6–9 mm. Unicolorous metallic green, blue or coppery. On oaks. A. laticornis Illig. 4–5 mm. Metallic olive-green. In woods.

4. Body very broad, almost triangular. On leaves. Trachys minuta L. Fig. 77, p. 89. 3–5 mm. Metallic black, el. with wavy bands of white pubescence. In fields and on poplar trees.

— Tibiae flattened.   EUCNEMIDAE

Melasis buprestoides L. Fig. 72, p. 87. 6–9 mm. Black, rather matt. In dead branches of beech, oak, ash, etc.

Figs. 74–82: 74 *Chalcophora mariana L., p. 86; 75 *Dicera berolinensis Hbst., p. 86; 76 *Chrysobothris affinis F., p. 88; 77 Trachys minuta L., p. 88; 78 Dascillus cervinus L., p. 82; 79 Cyphon variabilis Thunb., p. 81; 80 Dryops auriculatus Geoffr., p. 90; 81 Latelmis volckmari Panz., p. 90; 82 Heterocerus fossor Kiesw., p. 90.

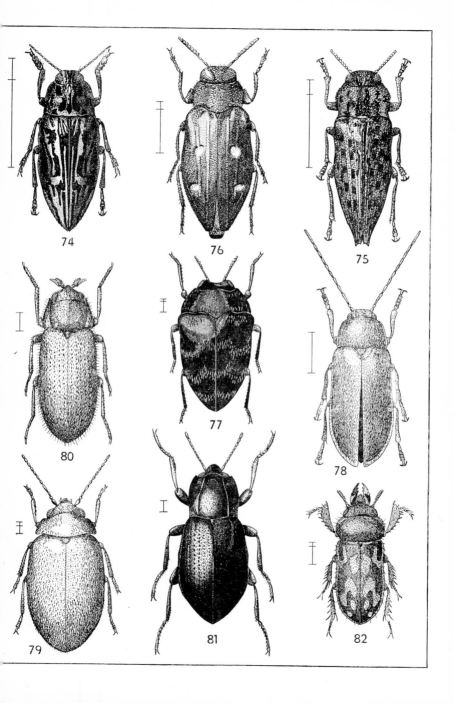

HYDROPHILI

1. Legs stout, tibiae with spines on the outer margin, last tarsal seg. short; mandibles of ♂ robust; black, el. with yellow markings. In sand or mud at the water's edge.

HETEROCERIDAE

> *Heterocerus fossor* Kiesw. Fig. 82, p. 89. 5–6 mm. Pubescence yellow.

— Legs more slender, tibiae slender, last tarsal seg. very long; mandibles not very robust.   DRYOPIDAE

> 1. *Dryops auriculatus* Geoffr. Fig. 80, p. 89. ± 5 mm. Ant. very short; black, clothed with a thick black pubescence. In mud at the water's edge.
> 2. *Latelmis* (also *Lathelmis*) *volckmari* Panz. Fig. 81, p. 89. ± 3 mm. Ant. long; black with a metallic reflection, almost glabrous. Under stones in running water.
> The GEORYSSIDAE, very small species (under 2 mm.), belong here. They live in wet places at the edges of streams; and are often covered with a thick layer of mud. There is one British species: *Georyssus crenulatus* Rossi. ± 1·5 mm. Shining black, glabrous.

CLAVICORNIA+BRACHYMERA

This group includes a large number of small species which are very variable in size and shape; they are found in a wide variety of habitats. The group is divided into families according to the number of tarsal segments—which is often different in the ♂ and ♀ of the same species. Determinations are very difficult to carry out without a microscope. The specimens should be carefully compared with the figures.

1. OSTOMIDAE (=TROGOSITIDAE)

Shape very variable.

> *Tenebroides mauritanicus* L. (Cadelle). Fig. 86, p. 93. 6–11 mm. Brownish-black, rather dull, glabrous. Ant.

base visible from above; apical ant. segs. thickened. In flour; it is not itself a pest, but preys on the larvae of pests.

2. Byturidae

Body oval, thickly pubescent. On flowers in woods. The larvae are often present in large numbers in raspberries and blackberries.

Byturus ochraceus Scriba. Fig. 87, p. 93. ± 5 mm. Yellow, clothed with a thick yellow pubescence; pthx. and underside sometimes darker. *B. tomentosus* F. (Raspberry Beetle). Very similar to the preceding species but smaller.

3. Nitidulidae

Body oval, convex or flat. Ant. club. 2–3-segmented.

Meligethes aeneus F. (Blossom Beetle). Fig. 88, p. 93. 2–3 mm. Metallic green, blue or violet, thickly pubescent; el. short, not covering the whole abd. On flowers. *Pria* (=*Laria*) *dulcamarae* Steph. Under 2 mm. Similar in shape to the preceding species. Reddish-brown with a darker patch surrounding the scutellum. On the flowers of Bitter Sweet (*Solanum dulcamara*). *Brachypterus urticae* F. ± 2 mm. Blackish-brown with a metallic reflection; ant. and legs lighter; pubescence brown. On the flowers of stinging nettles (*Urtica*). *Epuraea aestiva* L. 2–3 mm. Reddish-brown, clothed with fine sparse pubescence. On flowers. *Nitidula bipunctata* L. 3–5 mm. Similar in form to *Meligethes*. Dark-coloured, each el. with 1 round yellowish-red spot behind the middle. On bones and dry carcasses. *Ipidia quadrimaculata* Quens. Fig. 89, p. 93. ± 4 mm. Blackish-brown, el. with 4 red spots; body very flat. Under bark. *Pocadius ferrugineus* F. 3–4 mm. Body oval, brown or brownish-yellow; pubescence long. In puff-ball fungi (*Lycoperdon*).

4. Rhizophagidae

El. short, not covering the entire abdomen; body elongate, cylindrical; el. regularly punctate-striate; antennal club 1-segmented. Under bark in the galleries of wood-boring insects.

> *Rhizophagus dispar* Payk. Fig. 90, p. 93. 3–4 mm. Rusty-red, el. darker, with indistinct lighter patches.

5. Cucujidae

Body very flat.

> *Oryzaephilus surinamensis* L. (Saw-toothed Grain Beetle). Fig. 91, p. 93. ± 3 mm. Brown to yellow-brown. In houses and stored food; it is not a pest, but it feeds on the remains and excreta of pests. *Silvanus unidentatus* F. ± 2 mm. Brownish-red; similar to the preceding species but with the sides of the pthx. not serrate. Under the bark of deciduous trees. *Laemophloeus ferrugineus* Steph. (Red-rust Grain Beetle). ± 2 mm. Similar to the preceding species; reddish-brown; body very flat; ant. club distinct. In haystack refuse and in granaries.

6. Erotylidae

Body glabrous; el. punctate-striate, covering the whole abdomen. In tree fungi.

> *Triplax russica* L. Fig. 92, p. 95. 4·5–6·5 mm. Black, pnt. and abd. red.

Figs. 83–91: 83 *Dermestes lardarius* L. (Bacon Beetle), p. 93; 84 *Attagenus pellio* L. (Fur Beetle), p. 93; 85 *Byrrhus pilula* L. (Pill Beetle), p. 100; 86 *Tenebroides mauritanicus* L. (Cadelle), p. 90; 87 *Byturus ochraceus* Scriba, p. 91; 88 *Meligethes aeneus* F. (Blossom Beetle), p. 91; 89 *Ipidia 4-maculata* Quens., p. 91; 90 *Rhizophagus dispar* Payk., p. 92; 91 *Oryzaephilus surinamensis* L. (Saw-toothed Grain Beetle), p. 92.

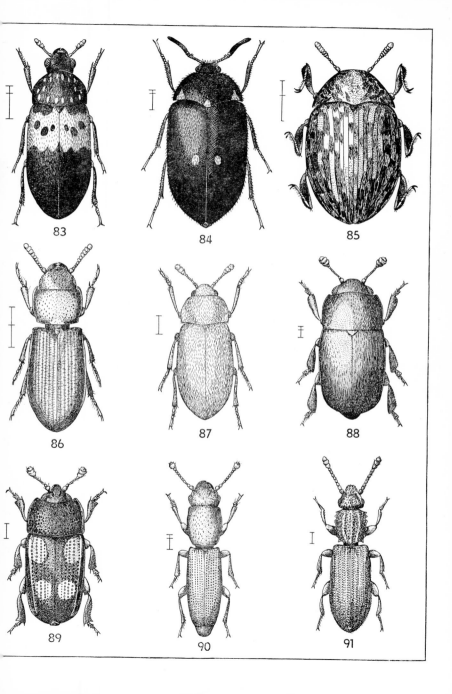

83

84

85

86

87

88

89

90

91

7. Cryptophagidae

Body small, pubescent; el. not punctate-striate.

> *Cryptophagus scanicus* L. Fig. 93, p. 95. ± 2 mm. Rusty-red, el. usually darker; sides of pthx. serrate. In dark places, such as stores and cellars.
> *Atomaria linearis* Steph. 1·2–1·5 mm. Dark brown, sides of pthx. not serrate. Under decaying vegetation.

8. Phalacridae

Body black, very shining; short and strongly convex. On flowers.

> *Phalacrus coruscus* Panz. Fig. 94, p. 95. 2–3·5 mm.

9. Lathridiidae

Tarsi 3-segmented; pthx. narrower than el.

> *Lathridius angusticollis* Gyllh. Fig. 95, p. 95. ± 2 mm. Brownish-black; el. with longitudinal ridges; pnt. with longitudinal keels. Under pine bark.
> *Enicmus minutus* L. (Plaster Beetle). ± 2 mm. Dark brown to black; pnt. without longitudinal keels; el. punctate-striate. In old wood and sometimes in newly built houses which have not yet dried out. The Beetles and larvae feed on moulds and mildews.
> *Corticaria fulva* Com. 1·5–2 mm. Yellowish-red; sides of pthx. curved; pnt. without longitudinal keels; el. punctate-striate. In cellars and under old straw.

Figs. 92–100: 92 *Triplax russica* L., p. 92; 93 *Cryptophagus scanicus* L., p. 94; 94 *Phalacrus coruscus* Panz., p. 94; 95 *Lathridius angusticollis* Gyllh., p. 94; 96 *Mycetophagus 4-pustulatus* L., p. 96; 97 *Ditoma crenata* F., p. 96; 98 *Cerylon histeroides* F., p. 96; 99 *Scymnus abietis* Payk., p. 96; 100 *Chilocorus bipustulatus* L., p. 97.

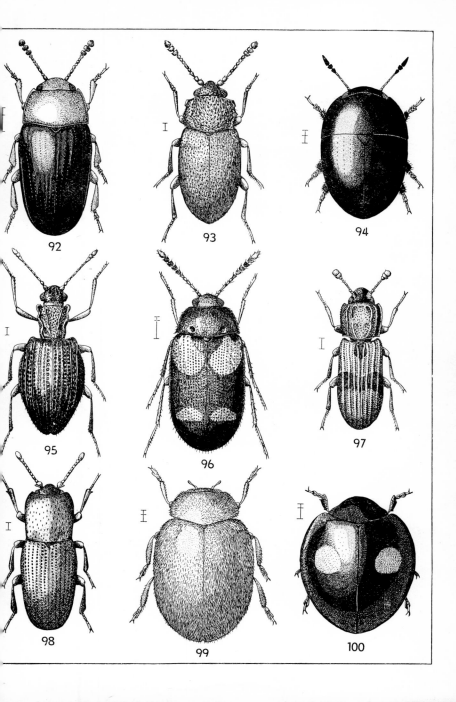

92

93

94

95

96

97

98

99

100

10. Mycetophagidae

Body flat, pubescent; el. with various different markings. In tree fungi.

> *Mycetophagus quadripustulatus* L. Fig. 96, p. 95. 5–6 mm. Black, underside, legs, hd. and ant. rusty-red, el. with yellowish-red markings.

11. Colydiidae

Shape very variable. Under bark and on wood.

> *Ditoma crenata* F. Fig. 97, p. 95. ± 3 mm. Black, el. with red markings. *Cerylon histeroides* F. Fig. 98, p. 95. ± 2 mm. Black to brown; body flat. Under pine bark.

12. Endomychidae

Body elongate-oval, antennae robust.

> *Mycetaea hirta* Marsh. 1·5–1·8 mm. Brownish-yellow, clothed with a thick yellow pubescence; ant. clubbed. In decaying wood. *Lycoperdina succincta* L. 4–4·5 mm. Red, el. with transverse black mark behind the middle; ant. not clubbed. In puff-ball fungi. *Endomychus coccineus* L. Colour Plate III, fac. p. 14. Glabrous. Under bark and in tree fungi.

13. Coccinellidae (Ladybirds, Ladybeetles)

Body more or less hemispherical; ant. short, terminating in a club.

> (*a*) Body pubescent.
> *Platynaspis luteorubra* Goeze. 2·5–3·5 mm. Body oval; black with 2 red spots on each el., one slightly in front of the middle the other near the apex. Under bark. *Scymnus abietis* Payk. Fig. 99, p. 95. 2·2–3 mm.

96

Reddish-yellow; pubescence long; body oval. On pine trees. *S. nigrinus* Kugel. 1·7–2 mm. Similar to the preceding species, unicolorous black. Chiefly on Scotch fir.

(b) Body glabrous. About 30 species which show a considerable variation in colour pattern between individuals, making it very difficult to separate the species. They are found on many different kinds of plants; both the adults and the larvae are useful to the gardener as they feed on Greenfly (Aphids). The most common species are figured. The colour varieties of *Adalia bipunctata* L. are shown on page 37.

The following 2 species live on pine trees. They are almost hemispherical, and the margins of the el. are broader and flatter than in the other species. *Chilocorus bipustulatus* L. Fig. 100, p. 95. 3–4 mm., and *Exochomus quadripustulatus* L. Similar to the preceding species but the el. with an additional patch on the shoulder. 3–5 mm. The colour and markings of both species are less variable than in the other species. The following species are less convex, and the margins of the el. are narrower, *Hippodamia tredecimpunctata* L. 4·5–7 mm. Base of pnt. not margined. In marshy places. *Adonia variegata* Goeze. 3–5·5 mm. Base of pnt. finely margined. In dry places. Both the preceding species are elongate-oval; el. red with round black markings. *Adalia bipunctata* L. Fig. 102, p. 99. 3·5–5·5 mm. Colour pattern very variable, but the position of the black spots never corresponds with the position of the spots in the following species. *Coccinella septempunctata* L. (7-spot Ladybird). Fig. 101, p. 99. 5·5–8 mm. On many different kinds of plants. *Propylaea quatuordecimpunctata* L. (14-spot). Fig. 104, p. 99. 3·5–4·5 mm. Yellow with black markings. Mainly in warm dry places. *Thea vigintiduopunctata* L. (22-spot Ladybird). Colour Plate III, fac. p. 14. In oak woods.

Anatis ocellata L. Fig. 103, p. 99. 8–12 mm. (the largest

British species). El. red with black markings, each spot often ringed with white. Generally in fir woods.

14. Cidae

Body small, ± cylindrical. In hard tree fungi.

Cis boleti Scop. Fig. 105, p. 99. ± 3 mm. Blackish-brown; el. strongly punctate.

15. Lyctidae (Powder-post Beetles)

Elongate cylindrical Beetles with punctate-striate elytra.

Lyctus brunneus Steph. 3–5 mm. Brownish-yellow, clothed with fine pubescence. A timber-yard pest.

16. Dermestidae

Body oval, clothed with hairs or scales. Prosternum without grooves for the reception of the legs and antennae.

Dermestes lardarius L. (Bacon Beetle, Larder Beetle). Fig. 83, p. 93. 7–9 mm. Black, basal half of el. yellow. A pest in houses. *Dermestes murinus* L. 7–9 mm. Black, upperside clothed with grey and black pubescence; femora ringed with white near the base. In dry carcasses and bones. **Dermestes laniarius* Illig. 6·5–8 mm. Similar to the preceding species but the femora not ringed with white. In dry carcasses. *Attagenus pellio* L. (Fur Beetle). Fig. 84, p. 93. 4·5–5·5 mm. Blackish-brown with small white spots. In skins and furs. *Anthrenus scrophulariae* L. Colour Plate III, fac. p. 14. Upperside clothed with coloured scales. On flowers. *A. museorum* L. (Museum

---

Figs. 101–9: 101 *Coccinella 7-punctata* L., p. 97; 102 *Adalia bipunctata* L., p. 97; 103 *Anatis ocellata* L., p. 97; 104 *Propylaea 14-punctata* L., p. 97; 105 *Cis boleti* Scop., p. 98; 106 *Bostrychus capucinus* L., p. 100; 107 **Anobium pertinax* L., p. 100; 108 *Stegobium paniceum* L. (Biscuit Beetle), p. 101; 109 *Ptilinus pectinicornis* L., p. 101.

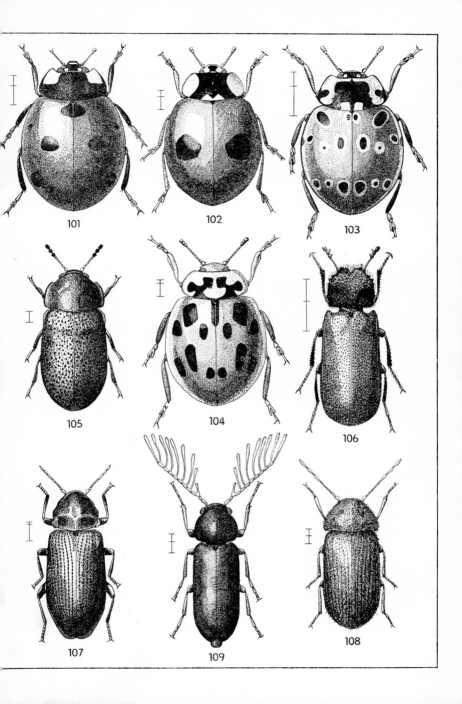

101

102

103

105

104

106

107

109

108

Beetle). 2–3 mm. Black, el. with 3 irregular transverse bands of yellow or white scales. A pest of insect collections; also on flowers.

17. BYRRHIDAE (Pill Beetles)

± globular, clothed with fine pubescence or scales. Prosternum with grooves for the reception of the legs.

Cytilus sericeus Forst. ± 5 mm. Ground colour metallic green. On paths in marshy places. *Byrrhus pilula* L. Fig. 85, p. 93. 7–11 mm. Brown, el. with longitudinal rows of darker and lighter spots. In woods.

TEREDILIA

1. Body elongate, cylindrical; ant. inserted at the side of the head.   2
— Abd. globular; legs long; ant. long, inserted on the front of the head between the eyes.

PTINIDAE (Spider Beetles)

Ptinus fur L. (White-marked Spider Beetle). Fig. 124, p. 107. 2–4 mm. Upperside with patches of white or yellow pubescence. In houses and on old wood. *Niptus hololeucus* Fald (Golden Spider Beetle). 4–4·5 mm. Body clothed with long dense golden-yellow pubescence. In houses, especially in dark places.

2. Apical segs. of ant. thickened   BOSTRYCHIDAE

Bostrychus capucinus L. Fig. 106, p. 99. 6–14 mm. Black, abd. and el. bright red. A pest of stored timber, especially oak and other hardwood.

— Apical segs. of ant. elongate, not clubbed.   ANOBIIDAE

Hedobia imperialis L. 4–4·5 mm. Dark-brown, upperside with a variable pattern of whitish squamose pubescence. On flowers and old wood. *Ernobius mollis* L. 4–5 mm. Rusty-red, el. not punctate-striate. In old coniferous wood. *Anobium* F. El. punctate-striate, pnt. strongly raised in the middle. In dry wood. **A. pertinax* L.

Fig. 107, p. 99. 4·5–5 mm. Brown to blackish-brown, posterior margin of pnt. with patches of yellow pubescence. *A. punctatum* Deg. (Furniture Beetle). 3–4 mm. Similar to the preceding species; reddish-brown. In old wood and furniture. The larva is well known as the "Woodworm". *Stegobium paniceum* L. (Biscuit Beetle, Drug Store Beetle). Fig. 108, p. 99. 2–4 mm. El. finely striate; pthx. not raised in the middle. Rusty-red, clothed with a dense silky pubescence. Pests of stored food products. *Ptilinus pectinicornis* L. Fig. 109, p. 99. 3–5 mm. Black, el. brown; ant. pectinate (♂) or strongly serrate (♀). In wood, the larvae may cause damage to furniture. *Xestobium rufovillosum* Deg. (Death Watch Beetle). 5–7 mm. Body cylindrical, el. irregularly punctate; dark brown with patches of yellowish pubescence. In old trees and in houses. The larvae often cause extensive damage to the woodwork of old buildings.

HETEROMERA

1. Base of ant. not visible from above, concealed by the expanded lateral margin of the head. Epipleurae very broad anteriorly. The shape of the body is very variable and often reminiscent of other families.

TENEBRIONIDAE

1. *Blaps mortisaga* L. Fig. 110, p. 103. 20–30 mm. Unicolorous black, rather dull. In cellars. Rare in the British Isles. *B. mucronata* Latr. (Cellar Beetle). 18–22 mm. Similar to the preceding species, but rather broader. In cellars, outbuildings, etc. They have a very characteristic strong smell.

2. *Melanimon tibiale* F. Fig. 111, p. 103. ± 4 mm. Black, rather dull. In sandy places.

3. *Opatrum sabulosum* L. Fig. 112, p. 103. 7–10 mm. Black, often encrusted with sand. In dry places.

4. *Crypticus quisquilius* L. Fig. 113, p. 103. 6–7 mm. Black, rather dull. The shape is very reminiscent of a Carabid Ground Beetle. Under stones in dry places.

5. *Diaperis boleti* L. Fig. 114, p. 103. 6–8 mm. Strongly convex; black, el. with reddish-yellow markings. In boleti (tree fungi), especially on birch. Rare in the British Isles.

6. *Hypophloeus unicolor* Pill. et Mitt. Fig. 115, p. 103. 5–6 mm. Body brown, shining, elongate, cylindrical. Under the bark of beech and elm trees.

7. *Tribolium madens* Charp. Fig. 116, p. 103. 4·5–5 mm. Blackish-brown to black; elongate. In old flour. This species has been introduced into Britain, but has not become established. *T. castaneum* Hbst. (Rust-red Flour Beetle). 3–4 mm. Similar to the preceding species but smaller. In flour; it is often found in large numbers in granaries and bakers' shops.

8. *Tenebrio molitor* L. (Flour Beetle. Larva: Yellow Meal Worm). Fig. 117, p. 103. 7–12 mm. Dark brown; el. punctate-striate. A pest in flour mills and granaries.

9. **Cylindronotus aeneus* Scop. Fig. 118, p. 103. 12–16 mm. Shining metallic bronze-brown. Under bark. *C. laevioctostriatus* Goeze. 8–10 mm. Black or dark brown. Very common under loose bark.

— Base of ant. visible from above, lateral margin of hd. not expanded.   2

2. Pnt. with a well-defined lateral margin.   3
— Pnt. without a well-defined lateral margin.   5
3. Claws pectinate.   ALLECULIDAE

Cteniopus flavus Scop. Fig. 122, p. 105. 7–9·5 mm. Unicolorous light yellow. On flowers. **Omophlus lepturoides* F. Fig. 123, p. 105. 11–16 mm. Black, el. red to yellow-brown. On flowering shrubs. *O. rufitarsis* Leske. 7–8 mm.

Figs. 110–18: 110 *Blaps mortisaga* L., p. 101; 111 *Melanimon tibiale* F., p. 101; 112 *Opatrum sabulosum* L., p. 101; 113 *Crypticus quisquilius* L., p. 101; 114 *Diaperis boleti* L., p. 102; 115 *Hypophloeus unicolor* Pill. et Mitt., p. 102; 116 *Tribolium madens* Charp., p. 102; 117 *Tenebrio molitor* L. (Flour Beetle), p. 102; 118 **Cylindronotus aeneus* Scop., p. 102.

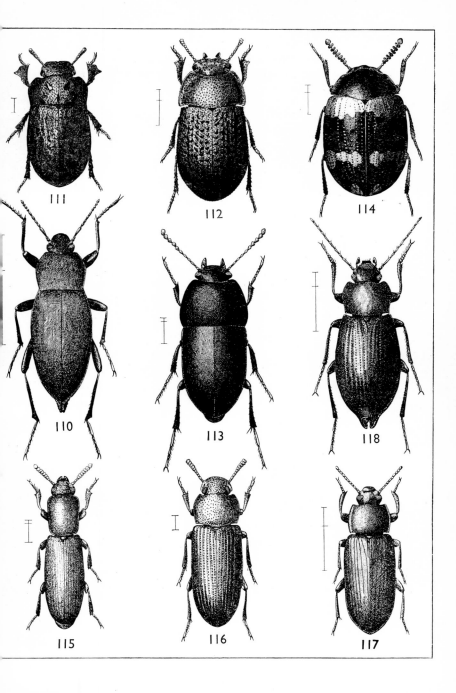

111

112

114

110

113

118

115

116

117

Similar to the preceding species. Shining black, el. yellow-brown. On Thrift (*Armeria maritima*).

— Claws simple, not pectinate. 4

4. Body flat, underside not strongly convex; tip of abd. not drawn out into a spine-like process. SERROPALPIDAE

> *Melandrya caraboides* L. Fig. 120, p. 105. 10–15 mm. Black with a metallic blue reflection. In old wood.

— Underside strongly convex; tip of abd. drawn out into a spine-like process. Very active species. On flowers.
MORDELLIDAE

> *Mordella aculeata* L. Fig. 119, p. 105. 4·5–6·5 mm. Black, clothed with dark, silky pubescence; pyg. drawn out into a long spine. *Mordellistena pumila* Gyllh. 3–4 mm. Black, much narrower than the preceding species. *Anaspis frontalis* L. 3–4 mm. Pyg. not drawn out into a spine-like process. Black, front of hd. and legs yellowish-red.

5. Hd. constricted behind the eyes. 6
— Hd. not constricted behind the eyes. 8

6. Small species, not more than 5 mm. long. ANTHICIDAE

> *Anthicus floralis* L. Fig. 128, p. 107. 3–3·5 mm. Brown or almost black, base of el., ant. and legs lighter. Under decaying vegetation.

— Larger species, more than 5 mm. long. 7

7. El. bright red. PYROCHROIDAE

> *Pyrochroa coccinea* L. (Cardinal Beetle). Colour Plate III, fac. p. 14. 14–15 mm. ant. serrate (♂); black, pnt. and el. red. Under bark and on flowers.

Figs. 119–23: 119 and 119a *Mordella aculeata* L., p. 104; 120 *Melandrya caraboides* L., p. 104; 121 *Lagria hirta* L., p. 106; 122 *Cteniopus flavus* Scop., p. 102; 123 *Omophlus lepturoides* F., p. 102.

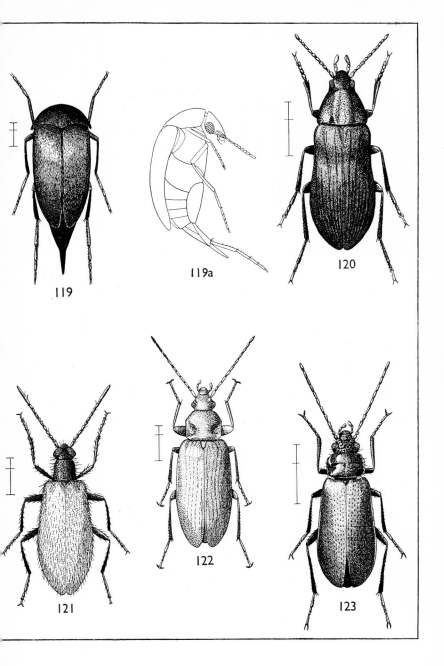

119

119a

120

121

122

123

— El. black or metallic, ant. neither serrate nor pectinate. The larvae are parasitic on bees. MELOIDAE

> 1. *Meloë* L. (Oil Beetles). El. short, $\pm$ overlapping at the base. *M. violaceus* Marsh. 10–32 mm. Dark blue to dark violet. *M. variegatus* Donov. Colour Plate III, fac. p. 14. 11–38 mm. Coloration metallic. In grassy places in spring.
> 2. *Lytta vesicatoria* L. (Blister Beetle, Spanish Fly). Fig. 129, p. 107. Bright metallic green; el. long, at most only the apex of the abd. exposed. On bushes, especially ash and privet.

8. Ant. long and thin. Soft-bodied insects. OEDEMERIDAE

> **Chrysanthia viridissima* L. Fig. 125, p. 107. 6–8 mm. Metallic green; el. not overlapping at the base, with indistinct longitudinal ridges. On flowers.
> **Oedemera femorata* Scop. Fig. 126, p. 107. 8–10 mm. Black with a metallic reflection, el. yellow; ♂ with hind femora thickened, ♀ with hind femora simple; el. divergent at the apex. *O. nobilis* Scop. 8–9 mm. Similar to the preceding species; metallic green, bluish-green or sometimes coppery. On flowers, especially in woods.

— Ant. thicker, moniliform. 9

9. Hd. short, without a snout-like prolongation; upperside thickly pubescent. LAGRIIDAE

> *Lagria hirta* L. Fig. 121, p. 105. 7–10 mm. Black, el. yellow-brown. On bushes.

— Hd. elongate, with a snout-like prolongation. PYTHIDAE

> *Salpingus castaneus* Panz. Fig. 127, p. 107. 3–3·5 mm. Dark brown; el. punctate-striate. On old wood.

Figs. 124–9: 124 *Ptinus fur* L. (White-marked Spider Beetle), p. 100; 125 **Chrysanthia viridissima* L., p. 106; 126 **Oedemera femorata* Scop., p. 106; 127 *Salpingus castaneus* Panz., p. 106; 128 *Anthicus floralis* L., p. 104; 129 *Lytta vesicatoria* L. (Blister Beetle, Spanish Fly), p. 106.

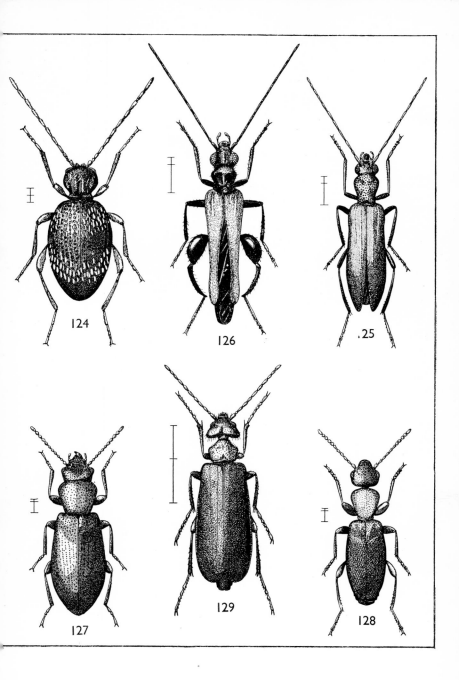

124

126

.25

127

129

128

1. Ant. strongly elbowed, apical segments enlarged on one side, not capable of closing together to form a compact club.   Lucanidae

> 1. *Lucanus cervus* L. (Stag Beetle). 25–75 mm. ♂ Fig. 132, p. 109 with enlarged antler-like mandibles; ♀ Fig. 132a, p. 109 with short mandibles. Black to brownish-black, rather dull. In oak woods; common in Kent and Surrey, and not uncommon in other southern counties; rare in the Midlands and North.
>
> 2. *Dorcus parallelopipedus* L. Fig. 133, p. 109. 19–32 mm. Dull black; mandibles of both sexes not exceptionally large. In woods.
>
> 3. **Systenocerus caraboides* L. Colour Plate III, fac. p. 14. 10–14 mm. Upperside metallic blue or green, underside black. In deciduous woods.
>
> 4. *Sinodendron cylindricum* L. Fig. 134, p. 109. 12–16 mm. Black, shining; body cylindrical; hd. with a small horn. Under the bark of deciduous trees.
>
> 5. **Ceruchus chrysomelinus* Hochw. 12–15 mm. Black, shining; body cylindrical. Ant. and palpi rusty-red; hd. without a horn. On beech trees, especially in mountainous regions.

— Ant. not elbowed, apical segments plate-like, capable of closing together to form a compact club.
         Scarabaeidae 2

2. Ant. with club short and broad, at least 2 apical segs. matt. Beetles living in dung and carcasses.   3

— Ant. generally with club segs. long and narrow, or if short somewhat shining; apical segs. bearing bristle-like setae. On flowers and leaves and also in wood.   6

Figs. 130–4: 130 **Valgus hemipterus* L., p. 114; 131 **Osmoderma eremita* Scop., p. 114; 132 *Lucanus cervus* L. ♂, 132a ♀ (Stag Beetle), p. 108; 133 *Dorcus parallelopipedus* L., p. 108; 134 *Sinodendron cylindricum* L., p. 108.

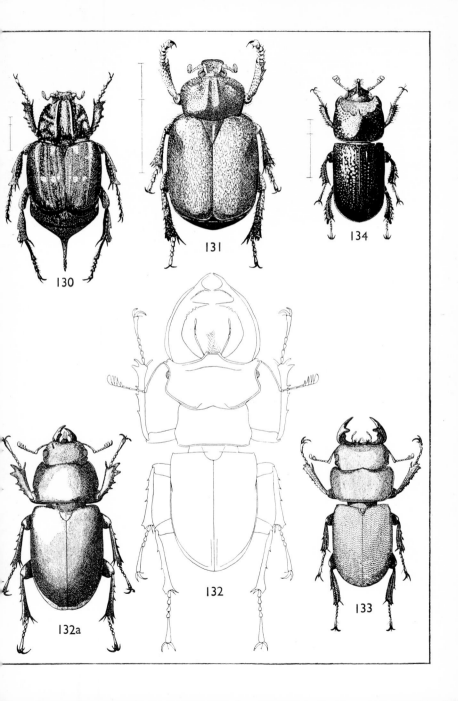

130

131

134

132a

132

133

3. Abd. 5-segmented.

> *Trox hispidus* Pontopp. Fig. 135, p. 111. 9–11 mm. Black; el. with longitudinal rows of coarse setae. On bones and dry carcasses. *T. scaber* L. 5·5–6 mm. Similar to the preceding species but much smaller and narrower. Very dull grey-black; el. with longitudinal rows of granules, intervals with rows of setae. In sandy places, and on dry carcasses and bones.

— Abd. 6-segmented. Beetles living in dung.   4
4. Posterior tibiae with 2 apical spines.   5
— Posterior tibiae with 1 apical spine.

> 1. *Copris lunaris* L. Fig. 141, p. 111. 17–25 mm. Black, very shining. Hd. of ♂ with a long, pointed horn, pnt. with 3 large protuberances anteriorly; ♀ with a short blunt horn, pnt. protuberances smaller. In sandy places.
> 2. **Oniticellus fulvus* Goeze. Fig. 139, p. 111. 7–10 mm. Scutellum clearly visible. Yellow with metallic green patches. In fresh dung.
> 3. *Onthophagus* Latr. (Dung Beetles). Scutellum not visible. *O. taurus* Schreib. Fig. 140, p. 111. 6–11 mm. Black. Hd. with 2 long curved horns (♂), or with transverse keels (♀). *O. fracticornis* Preyssl. 6–9 mm. Black with a metallic reflection; el. yellow with irregular black markings. *O. ovatus* L. ± 5 mm. Unicolorous black, without a metallic reflection.

5. Mandibles not visible from above.

> *Aphodius* Illig. (Dung Beetles). *A. fossor* L. 8–12 mm. Shining black, el. sometimes red; body strongly convex. *A. fimetarius* L. Fig. 136, p. 111. 5·5–6 mm. Black, el. red, with very distinct longitudinal grooves. *A. merdarius* F.

Figs. 135–41: 135 *Trox hispidus* Pontopp., p. 110; 136 *Aphodius fimetarius* L., p. 110; 137 *A. luridus* F. (Dung Beetle), p. 112; 138 *Geotrupes vernalis* L. (Dor Beetle), p. 112; 139 **Oniticellus fulvus* Goeze, p. 110; 140 *Onthophagus taurus* Schreib., p. 110; 141 *Copris lunaris* L., p. 110.

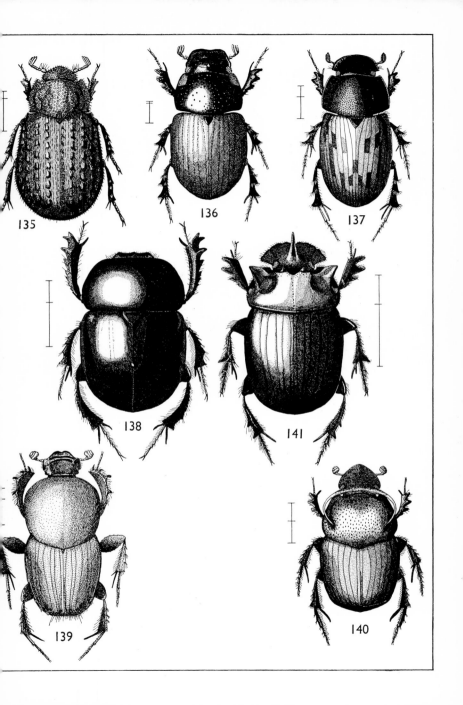

4·5–5 mm. Black, legs brown, el. yellow to yellow-brown with the suture darker. *A. luridus* F. Fig. 137, p. 111. 6–9 mm. Black, el. yellow-brown with black markings. *A. prodromus* Brahm. 4–7 mm. Pnt. and el. yellow-brown; each el. with a large clouded spot. *Pleurophorus caesus* Panz. 2·5–3 mm. Black, upperside rather dull, legs red.

— Mandibles visible from above, large species.

Geotrupes Latr. (Dor Beetles) *G. vernalis* L. Fig. 138, p. 111. 12–18 mm. Very shining, black with a blue or green reflection. El. almost smooth (very finely and indistinctly punctate-striate). *G. stercorosus* Scriba. 12–18 mm. Less strongly shining than the previous species; blue to blue-black. El. with fine and distinct striae. In dung. *G. stercorarius* L. 16–24 mm. El. dark, metallic; with 7 deep longitudinal grooves. In dung. *G. mutator* Marsh. Very similar to the preceding species but el. with 9 longitudinal grooves.

6. Mandibles visible from above, large species.

Oryctes nasicornis L. Fig. 146, p. 115. 25–40 mm. Shining brown; hd. with horn (♂) or without horn (♀). In decaying wood.

— Mandibles not visible from above.   7

7. Anterior lateral margins of el. deeply emarginate.

1. *Epicometis hirta* Poda. 8–12 mm. Black with isolated small white spots; upperside clothed with long, sparse pubescence. On flowers.
2. *Cetonia aurata* L. (Rose Chafer). Colour Plate IV, fac. p. 30. 14–20 mm. Bright metallic green; anterior process of the mesosternum globular. On roses and other flowering bushes.
3. *Potosia cuprea* F. (subspecies *metallica* Hbst. in Britain). Olive-green, less strongly shining than the previous species; anterior process of the mesosternum truncate.

Often occurs together with *C. aurata.* *Liocola lugubris* Hbst. 9–15 mm. Similar to the preceding species. Upperside often with many white spots. 5th abd. sternite with a longitudinal groove.

— Anterior lateral margins of el. not emarginate.   8

8. Posterior margins of mid and hind tibiae without sharp transverse ridges.   9

— Posterior margins of mid and hind tibiae with sharp transverse ridges.   10

9. Tarsal claws of equal size and shape.

1. Last 3 ant. segs. lamellate; body reddish-yellow to brownish-yellow; less than 20 mm. long. On deciduous trees and on the grass. Active mainly in the evening and at night. *Rhizotrogus aestivus* Oliv. Fig. 142, p. 115. 12–18 mm. Ant. 10-segmented. *Amphimallon solstitialis* L. (Midsummer Chafer). 14–18 mm. Similar to the preceding species. Ant. 9-segmented.

2. Last 4–7 ant. segs. lamellate *Polyphylla fullo* F. [Walker]. Colour Plate III, fac. p. 14. 24–34 mm. Ground colour brown or blackish-brown; ant. lamellae very large (♂). In sandy regions. *Melolontha* F. (Cockchafers). Upperside evenly clothed with long, fine pubescence; abd. sternites with a patch of white pubescence on either side. The larvae do a great deal of damage as they feed on the roots of many plants. *M. hippocastani* F. Fig. 143, p. 115. 20–25 mm. Pyg. shorter, very slightly thickened at the apex. *M. melolontha* L. (Common Cockchafer). 20–26 mm. Pyg. longer, gradually narrowed towards the apex. Common and generally distributed in the British Isles: often found in large numbers flying round trees.

— Claws of unequal length.

1. Clypeus elongate, snout-like. *Anisoplia* Lap. *A. segetum* Hbst. 10–12 mm. Metallic green, el. reddish-brown to reddish-yellow. *A. agricola* Poda. Colour

Plate III, fac. p. 14. 11–14 mm. In grain fields and on grass.

2. Clypeus not elongate.

Upperside glabrous. *Anomala* Sam. *A. aenea* Deg. Colour Plate III, fac. p. 14. 12–15 mm. Coloration metallic; el. sometimes yellow. In fields in sandy regions.

Upperside pubescent. *Phyllopertha horticola* L. (Garden Chafer, Bracken Clock). Fig. 145, p. 115. 8–12 mm. Dark metallic green to blue, el. usually brown. On bushes. Common in Britain.

3. Clypeus not elongate.

Upperside clothed with scales and setae. *Hoplia* Illig. *H. farinosa* Deg. Fig. 145, p. 115. 9–11 mm. Upperside clothed with green, yellow or brown scales, underside with golden scales. On flowers in mountainous regions. *H. philanthus* Fuessl. 6·5–8 mm. Black, el. reddish-brown, scales on upperside scanty, yellowish; but thick and bluish on the underside. On flowering shrubs and bushes.

10. El. depressed in the centre; ♀ with elongate spine-like pyg.

Valgus hemipterus L. Fig. 130, p. 109. 7–9 mm. Black, clothed with black and white scales. On flowers and bushes.

— El. convex, larger species; ♀ without elongate spine-like pyg.

Osmoderma eremita Scop. Fig. 131, p. 109. 20–30 mm. Blackish-brown with a metallic reflection. These Beetles have a strong smell. On deciduous trees. *Gnorimus nobilis* L. Colour Plate IV, fac. p. 30. 14–18 mm. Bright metallic green to coppery. On flowering shrubs; rather

---

Figs. 142–6: 142 *Rhizotrogus aestivus* Oliv., p. 113; 143 *Melolontha hippocastani* F. (Cockchafer), p. 113; 144 *Phyllopertha horticola* L. (Garden Chafer), p. 114; 145 *Hoplia farinosa* Deg., p. 114; 146 *Oryctes nasicornis* L., p. 112.

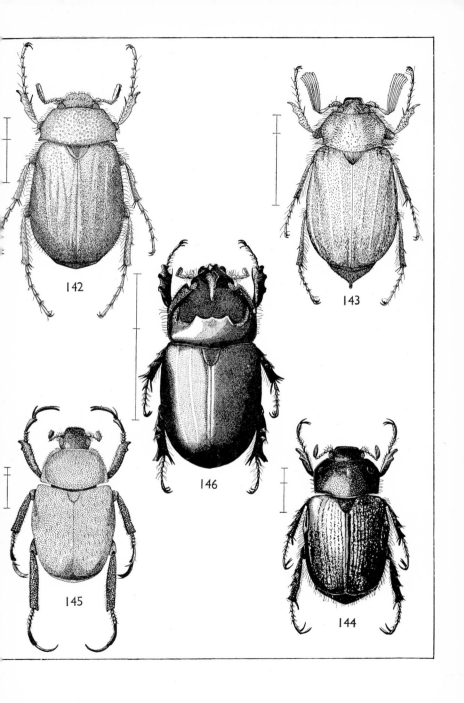

142

143

146

145

144

rare in Britain. *Trichius fasciatus* L. (Bee Beetle). Colour
Plate IV, fac. p. 30. 10–13 mm. On flowers in wooded
regions.

PHYTOPHAGA

1. El. without distinct epipleurae; hd. small, ant. serrate;
pyg. very large, not covered by el.

BRUCHIDAE (=MYLABRIDAE) (Pulse Beetles)
Bruchus pisorum L. (Pea Beetles). Fig. 190, p. 137. 3–5 mm.
Yellowish to brownish, with black, dark brown or
occasionally white markings. In peas; pale round blister-
like spots on the surface of the peas indicate that the
beetles are active inside.

— El. epipleurae distinct, at least at the base.   2

2. Tibiae with distinct apical spurs; body usually long and
narrow; ant. stout and long, inserted close to the eyes.

CERAMBYCIDAE (Longhorn Beetles)
— Front and middle tibiae without apical spurs; body
usually shorter and rounder; ant. long and thin or short
and stout, inserted between or in front of the eyes.

CHRYSOMELIDAE (Leaf Beetles)

CERAMBYCIDAE

1. Ant. inserted close to the front or the side of the eyes.   2
— Ant. inserted in the emargination of the eyes.   12

2. Ant. glabrous; large species.

Prionus coriarius L. (Sawer Beetle). Fig. 147, p. 119.
27–60 mm. Ant. serrate, more strongly in ♂ than ♀.
Blackish-brown, rather shining. From both deciduous
and coniferous wood.

Ergates faber L. Fig. 148, p. 119. 27–60 mm. Ant. not
serrate, brown to reddish-brown. In pine woods. This
species is occasionally imported in coniferous timber.

* *Tragosoma depsarium* L. 16–30 mm. Similar to the preceding species but smaller. Sides of pthx. with one spine.
In mountainous regions.

116

— Ant. clothed with scales or hairs. 3
3. El. long, covering almost the entire abd. 4
— El. much shorter, leaving the wings exposed. The wings are not capable of being folded away beneath the el.

Molorchus minor L. Fig. 155, p. 121. 8–13 mm. Black, el., ant. and legs yellow-brown or rusty-red. On flowers and from coniferous wood. **Necydalis major* L. 19–32 mm. El. red, body mainly brown. On willows and poplars: rare. *Leptideela brevipennis* Muls. 3–5 mm. Dark brown to brownish-red, pthx. sometimes lighter. Usually from wickerwork.

4. Front coxae small and globular, not attaining 1/2 length of pthx. Body usually parallel-sided. 8
— Front coxae large, almost attaining 1/2 length of pthx. Body usually narrowing posteriorly. 5
5. Pthx. with a tubercle at each side. 6
— Pthx. ± globular, without a tubercle at each side. 7
6. El. with 2 to 4 longitudinal ridges; prothoracic tubercles sharp-pointed.

Rhagium F. On newly-felled wood and on flowers, especially *Umbelliferae* (Fool's parsley, etc.). **R. sycophanta* Schr., Colour Plate IV, fac. p. 30. 18–25 mm. In deciduous woods. *R. mordax* Deg. 14–19 mm. Similar to the preceding species but smaller and without a yellow longitudinal mark on the pnt. *R. inquisitor* L. 12–15 mm. Smaller than the preceding species; el. ridges more strongly raised. Black, pubescence mottled grey and white. Found in the north of the British Isles. *R. bifasciatum* F. 14–18 mm. Almost black, pubescence sparse; el. with 2 oblique reddish-yellow glabrous bands.

— El. without longitudinal ridges.

*Toxotus cursor L. Fig. 149, p. 119. ♀ 16–23 mm. ♂ entirely black, narrower; ♀ black, ant. and legs partly red-brown, and el. with lateral margin and suture red-brown; ant.

inserted between the eyes. In coniferous woods. *Stenocorus meridianus* L. 15–24 mm. Similar in shape to the preceding species; ant. inserted near the margin of the eyes. Colour very variable, el. black (♂) or yellow (♀). In deciduous woods. **Pachyta quadrimaculata* L. Colour Plate IV, fac. p. 30. 11–19 mm. On flowers in mountainous regions. **Gaurotes virginea* L. Fig. 150, p. 119. 9–12 mm. Black, abd. and occasionally also pnt. red, el. blue. On flowers in mountainous regions.

7. El. parallel-sided.

> *Acmaeops collaris* L. Fig. 151, p. 119. 7–9 mm. Black, pthx. and abd. red. On flowers in woods.

— El. strongly tapering towards the apex, usually brightly coloured.

> 1. *Leptura* L. Posterior angles of pthx. obtuse or rounded. *L. rubra* L. 12–18 mm. Black, el. yellow (♂), or pthx. and el. red (♀). In coniferous woods. *L. livida* F. Fig. 154, p. 121. Black, ant. black, el. yellow. On flowers. **L. maculicornis* Deg. Fig. 153, p. 121. 8–10 mm. Similar to the preceding species but the bases of the middle ant. segs. yellow. On flowers in woods. *Judolia cerambyciformis* Schr. Colour Plate IV, fac. p. 30. 7–11 mm. On flowers in woods. Southern species.
>
> 2. *Strangalia* Serv. Posterior angles of pthx. acute. *S. quadrifasciata* L. 13–18 mm. Black, el. with 4 zigzag transverse yellow bands. Shape similar to *S. maculata* Poda. On flowers. **S. maculata* Poda. Colour Plate V, fac. p. 34. Imported in wood: on flowers in woods in Europe. *S. melanura* L. Fig. 152, p. 119. 7–9 mm. El. yellow with apex black (♂), or red with black markings (♀). On flowers.

Figs. 147–52: 147 *Prionus coriarius* L. (Sawer Beetle), p. 116; 148 *Ergates faber L., p. 116; 149 *Toxotus cursor L., p. 117; 150 *Gaurotes virginea* L., p. 118; 151 *Acmaeops collaris* L., p. 118; 152 *Strangalia melanura* L., p. 118.

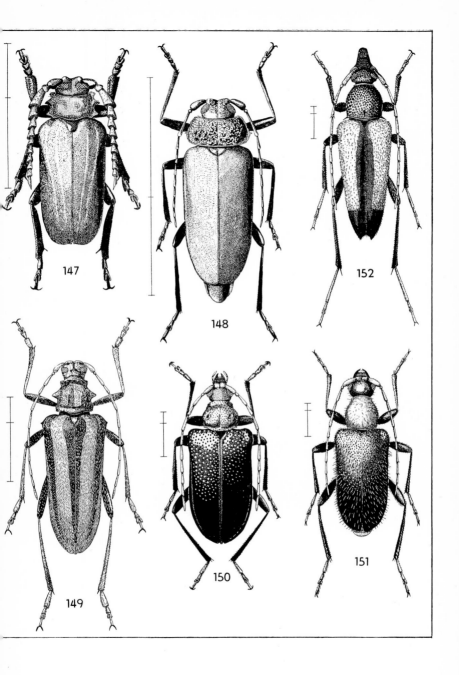

147

148

149

150

151

152

8. Distance between hind margins of eyes less than distance between ant. insertions; el. without transverse bands (with the exception of *Rosalia alpina* L.), more or less unicolorous species. 9

— Distance between hind margins of eyes greater than distance between ant. insertions; el. with transverse pubescent bands; pthx. globular.

> *Clytus rhamni Germ. Colour Plate V, fac. p. 34. 6–12 mm. Black, el. with yellow pubescent markings; punctuation of pnt. and el. coarse. On flowers. *C. arietis* L. (Wasp Beetle). 13–19 mm. Similar to the preceding species but larger. Punctuation of pnt. and el. fine and very dense. **Plagionotus arcuatus* L. Fig. 161, p. 123. 9–20 mm. Black, with yellow markings. Occasionally imported in timber: on flowers in Europe.

9. Pthx. ± globular or transverse, not constricted in front or behind. 11

— Pthx. distinctly constricted in front or behind. 10

10. Body very small.

> *Gracilia minuta* F. 4·5–6 mm. Brown, ant. and legs lighter. Chiefly from dead twigs and wickerwork, and also on flowering bushes.

— Body large.

> *Cerambyx cerdo* L. 30–55 mm. Dark brown. On oak. *C. scopolii* Fuessl. Fig. 156, p. 121. 18–30 mm. Similar to the preceding species but smaller and entirely black. On flowers. *Aromia moschata* L. (Musk Beetle). Colour Plate V, fac. p. 34. 20–35 mm. Usually bright metallic green. On willows (*Salix* species).

Figs. 153–8: 153 **Leptura maculicornis* Deg., p. 118; 154 *L. livida* F., p. 118; 155 *Molorchus minor* L., p. 117; 156 *Cerambyx scopolii* Fuessl., p. 122; 157 *Pyrrhidium sanguineum* L., p. 122; 158 *Callidium violaceum* L., p. 122.

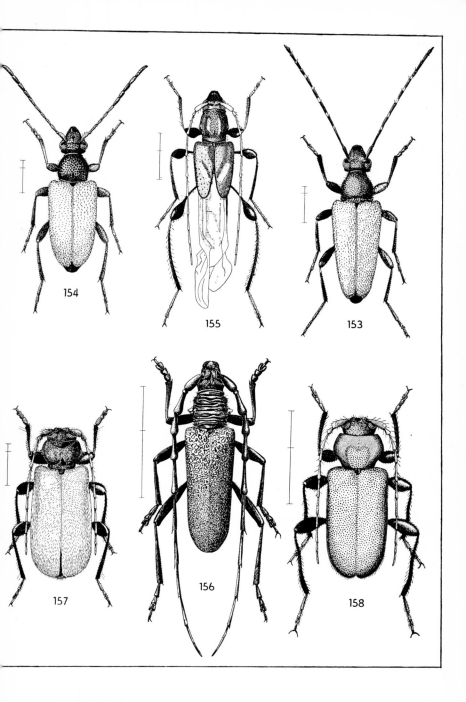

11. El. with distinct markings; body large.

> *Rosalia alpina* L. Colour Plate V, fac. p. 34. 22–26 mm
> Blue with black markings. On bushes in mountainous
> regions. Introduced, chiefly in beech.

— El. unicolorous, or almost unicolorous.

> *Pyrrhidium sanguineum* L. Fig. 157, p. 121. 9–11 mm.
> Black, el. and pnt. clothed with dense red pubescence,
> giving the Beetle a bright red appearance. Under bark
> and on felled timber. *Callidium violaceum* L. Fig. 158,
> p. 121. 15–25 mm. Blue or violet. Under bark and from
> dead and seasoned coniferous timber. *Phymatodes testaceus*
> L. (Tanbark Borer). 8–13 mm. Similar to the preceding
> species but narrower. Upperside very finely and sparsely
> punctate. Coloration very variable, brown to metallic
> blue. On newly-felled timber. *Hylotrupes bajulus* L.
> (House Longhorn). Fig. 159, p. 123. 8–20 mm. Black,
> sides of pthx. with outstanding greyish-white hairs; el.
> with 2 distinct white transverse bands near the middle.
> From dry, seasoned coniferous timbers; the larvae may
> cause severe damage to the structural timbers of houses.
> *Tetropium castaneum* L. Fig. 160, p. 123. 10–18 mm.
> Black, el. and legs often brown. On coniferous wood.
> *T. gabrielli* Weise (Larch Longhorn). 10–15 mm.
> Similar to the preceding species; entirely black.

12. Sides of pthx. with a single sharp spine.

> *Lamia textor* L. Fig. 162, p. 123. 14–30 mm. Black with a
> few scattered patches of yellow pubescence. On willows
> (*Salix* species). *Acanthocinus aedilis* L. (Timberman).

Figs. 159–66: 159 *Hylotrupes bajulus* L. (House Longhorn), p. 122;
160 *Tetropium castaneum* L., p. 122; 161 *Plagionotus arcuatus* L., p. 120;
162 *Lamia textor* L., p. 124; 163 *Acanthocinus aedilis* L. (Timberman),
p. 124; 164 *Saperda populnea* L. (Poplar Longhorn), p. 124; 165 *Phytoecia
coerulescens* Scop., p. 124; 166 *Oberea oculata* L., p. 124.

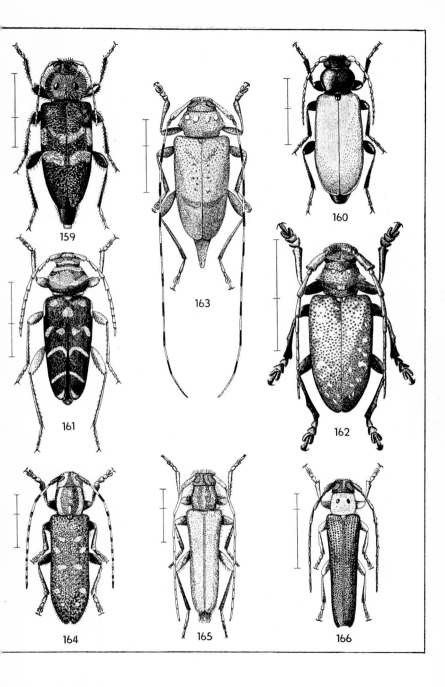

159

160

161

163

162

164

165

166

Fig. 163, p. 123. 13–20 mm. Brown to grey, with indistinct darker markings; ant. very long—up to 10 cm. ($\male$) or shorter ($\female$); $\female$ with pyg. produced into a tubular process. Northern species; rare, but frequently imported in pine wood.

— Sides of pthx. without lateral spines or processes.

> *Saperda carcharias* L. 22–30 mm. Black, clothed with dense yellow or grey pubescence. Chiefly from poplars. *S. populnea* L. (Poplar Longhorn). Fig. 164, p. 123. 9–14 mm. Black, el. with scattered patches of dense yellow pubescence. From poplars and willows. **Phytoecia coerulescens* Scop. Fig. 165, p. 123. 9–14 mm. Black, clothed with dense blue or green pubescence. On flowers, especially Viper's bugloss (*Echium*). *P. cylindrica* L. 6–10 mm. Similar to the preceding species. Black, pubescence dark, front femora and tibiae yellow. On *Umbelliferae* (Fool's parsley, etc.). *Oberea oculata* L. Fig. 166, p. 123. 16–20 mm. Yellow-brown, el. black clothed with grey pubescence, patches on hd. and pnt. black. On willows (*Salix* species).

Chrysomelidae (Leaf Beetles)

1. Mouth-parts clearly visible from in front or above.	2
— Mouth-parts not visible from in front or above.	13
2. Hd. retracted into pthx. up to the eyes.	5
— Hd. prominent, not retracted into pthx.	3
3. El. punctate-striate.	4
— El. confusedly punctate.	

> *Zeugophora subspinosa* F. Fig. 169, p. 125. $\pm$ 3·5 mm. Yellow, el. and apex of ant. black; upperside clothed with fine pubescence. On birches.

Figs. 167–71: 167 *Donacia simplex* F., p. 126; 168 *Lema lichenis* Voet, p. 126; 169 *Zeugophora subspinosa* F., p. 124; 170 **Labidostomis longimana* L., p. 127; 171 **Clytra laeviuscula* L., p. 126.

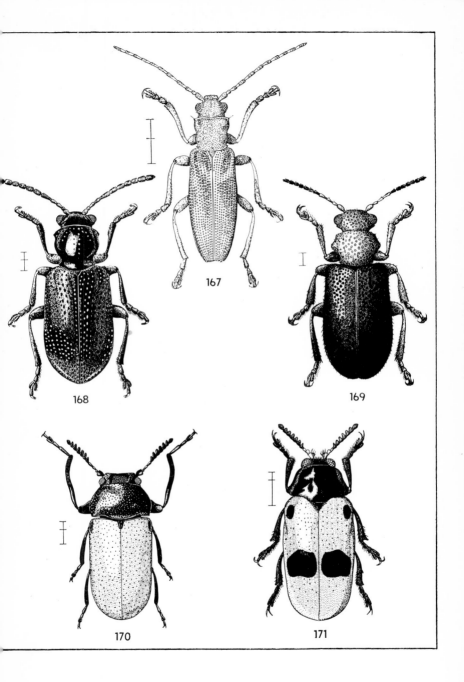

167

168

169

170

171

4. 1st ant. seg. elongate and thickened; larger species (7–12 mm.) often metallic. On water plants, and sometimes even in the water.

> *Donacia aquatica* L. El. golden-green with purple longitudinal stripes. *D. simplex* F. Fig. 167, p. 125. 7–9 mm. El. unicolorous coppery-bronze to greenish-bronze, legs and ant. partly reddish. *D. cinerea* Hbst. 7–10 mm. Dull grey or coppery, clothed with fine grey pubescence.

— 1st ant. seg. globular, not elongate; smaller species (3–7 mm.), not living on water plants.

> 1. Tarsal claws fused at the base: *Lema* F. *L. lichenis* Voet. Fig. 168, p. 125. 3–5 mm. Unicolorous metallic blue. *L. melanopa* L. (Cereal Leaf Beetle). Similar to the preceding species; el. blue, hd., pnt. and legs reddish-yellow. In fields and meadows.
>
> 2. Tarsal claws not fused at the base; el. unicolorous red. *Lilioceris lilii* L. 6–7 mm. Similar to the preceding species but larger; almost unicolorous red.
>
> 3. *Crioceris asparagi* L. (Asparagus Beetle). Colour Plate V, fac. p. 34. ± 5 mm. Similar to the preceding species.

5. Pyg. small, entirely hidden by the el.; body oval.   7
— Pyg. large, not entirely covered by the el.; body cylindrical.   6
6. Ant. long, filiform.

> *Cryptocephalus bipunctatus* L. Colour Plate V, fac. p. 34. 4–6 mm. On flowers. The markings are very variable, there may be 1 to 4 black spots or a longitudinal black mark on each el. *C. aureolus* Suff. 5·5–7·5 mm. Similar to the preceding species; bright metallic green.

— Ant. short, apical segs. serrate.

> *Clytra laeviuscula* L. Fig. 171, p. 125. Black, el. orange-red with dark markings; very shining. On pastures. *C. quadripunctata* L. 7–11 mm. Very similar to the preceding

species, but the black spots on the el. are smaller. On herbage. *Labidostomis longimana L. Fig. 170, p. 125. 4–6 mm. Green or blue, el. yellow, often with a black patch on the shoulder. Front legs of ♂ very long. In dry places. *L. tridentata* L. 6–8·5 mm. Very similar to the preceding species but larger. On trees; rather rare.

7. Ant. insertions far apart, in front of the eyes.   8
— Ant. insertions close together, between the eyes.   12
8. Pthx. ± cylindrical, much narrower than the el.; 3rd tarsal seg. deeply emarginate.

Adoxus obscurus L. Fig. 172, p. 129. 4·5–6 mm. Black or brown, pubescence grey (subspecies *obscurus* L. on Willow-Herb) or pubescence yellow (ssp. *vitis* F. in vineyards). *Chrysochus asclepiadeus* Pall. 8–10 mm. Bright metallic blue to violet, very shining. On *Vincetoxicum officinale*.

— Pthx. not cylindrical, with a distinct lateral margin; 3rd tarsal seg. weakly or indistinctly emarginate.   9
9. Posterior inner margin of epipleurae fringed with hairs.

Leptinotarsa decemlineata Say (Colorado Potato Beetle). Colour Plate VI, fac. p. 42. ± 10 mm. A dangerous foreign potato pest, which may appear in this country. If the Beetle, or the yellow larva, are found eating the potato leaves, they should at once be put in a tin box and sent to the Ministry of Agriculture (28 Milton Road, Harpenden, Herts.) with a letter stating the exact place where they were found, and the name and address of the finder. *Chrysolina* (=*Chrysomela*) *menthastri* Suff. 7–10 mm. Bright metallic green. On Tansy (*Tanacetum vulgare*) and Mint (*Mentha* species). *C. staphylea* L. 7–10 mm. Brown with an indistinct metallic reflection. In damp places. *C. varians* Schall. Fig. 173, p. 129. 5–7 mm. Strongly convex; metallic green, blue or bright red. On St. John's Wort (*Hypericum*). *Dlochrysa fastuosa* Scop. Colour Plate VI, fac. p. 42. 5–7 mm. Coloration metallic. On Labiatae (nettles, etc.). *Chrysochloa* Hope. Very similar

127

in colour to the preceding species, but larger in size. There are numerous species in mountainous regions in Europe; the species are very difficult to separate.

— Epipleurae glabrous. 10
10. El. confusedly punctate. 11
— El. punctate-striate.

> *Phytodecta viminalis* L. Fig. 178, p. 131. 6–9 mm. Black, upperside red with variable black markings. On willows (*Salix* species). *Phyllodecta vitellinae* L. (Brassy Willow Beetle). Fig. 179, p. 131. 4–5 mm. Dark, metallic; elongate. On willows (*Salix* species).

11. Wings absent, el. fused at the suture. Large unicolorous species.

> **Timarcha metallica* Laich. 6–10 mm. Metallic bronze-brown, rather dull. Under stones in mountainous regions. *T. goettingensis* L. 8–13 mm. Punctuation coarse; black or blue-black. *T. tenebricosa* F. (Bloody-nose Beetle). Fig. 180, p. 131. 10–20 mm. Punctuation fine; black or blue-black. On grass and low plants. The Beetles extrude a bright-red fluid from the mouth when handled.

— Wings present, el. not fused at the suture. Smaller species.

> 1. Pthx. much narrower than el.; *Chrysomela* (=*Melasoma*) *populi* L. Fig. 176, p. 129. 8–12 mm. Black, el. red. On willows (*Salix* species). *C. aenea* L. 6–9 mm. Metallic green, blue or coppery. On alders. **C. vigintipunctata* L. Fig. 177, p. 131. 6–8·5 mm. Black with a metallic reflection, el. yellow or reddish, with black patches. On willows (*Salix* species).
> 2. Pthx. almost as wide as el. *Gastrophysa viridula* Deg. 4–6 mm. Elongate; unicolorous metallic green; abd. of ♀

Figs. 172–6: 172 *Adoxus obscurus L., p. 127; 173 *Chrysolina varians* Schall., p. 127; 174 *Gastrophysa polygoni* L., p. 130; 175 *Plagiodera versicolora* Laich, p. 130; 176 *Chrysomela populi* L., p. 128.

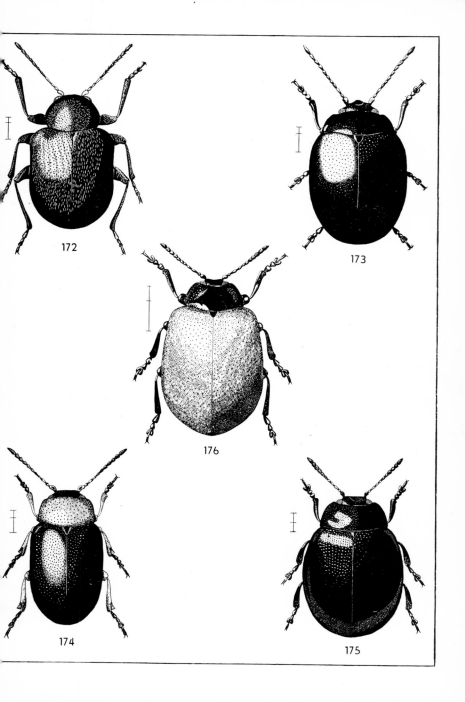

172

173

176

174

175

swollen. On Docks (*Rumex*) and Knotgrass (*Polygonum*). *G. polygoni* L. Fig. 174, p. 129. 4–6 mm. Like the preceding species but less shining. Pthx. red. *Plagiodera versicolora* Laich. Fig. 175, p. 129. 2·5–5 mm. Body rounded; dark metallic blue to bluish-green. On willows (*Salix* species).

12. Hind femora normal, not thickened (species not able to jump).

  1. Body not metallic: *Galeruca tanaceti* L. Fig. 181, p. 131. 6–12 mm. Glabrous, black. On low grass. *Lochmaea capreae* L. 4–6 mm. Glabrous, black, pnt. and el. yellow. On willow (*Salix* species). *Galerucella calmariensis* L. 4–5 mm. Black, upperside reddish-yellow with indistinct darker patches, clothed with thick, fine pubescence. In damp meadows.
  2. Body metallic blue or violet. *Agelastica alni* L. Fig. 182, p. 133. 6–8 mm. On alders.

— Hind femora thickened, jumping Beetles (Flea Beetles).

  Numerous small, mainly monophagous species; a few species are garden pests.
  Phyllotreta undulata Kutsch. (Small Striped Flea Beetle). Fig. 183, p. 133. 2–2·5 mm. Blue or greenish, with yellow markings. *P. atra* F. (Turnip Flea Beetle, Turnip Fly). ± 2 mm. Unicolorous black. Both species are turnip pests. *Altica* (=*Haltica*) *oleracea* L. Fig. 184, p. 133. 3–4 mm. Blue or green. On bushes.

13. Body broad and flat, hd. not visible from above, margins of pthx. and el. explanate (Tortoise Beetles).

  Cassida viridis L. Colour Plate VI, fac. p. 42. 7–9 mm. Grass-green, matt. On Labiatae, especially Mint

---

Figs. 177–81: 177 **Chrysomela 20-punctata* L., p. 128; 178 *Phytodecta viminalis* L., p. 128; 179 *Phyllodecta vitellinae* L. (Brassy Willow Beetle), p. 128; 180 *Timarcha tenebricosa* F. (Bloody-nose Beetle), p. 128; 181 *Galeruca tanaceti* L., p. 130.

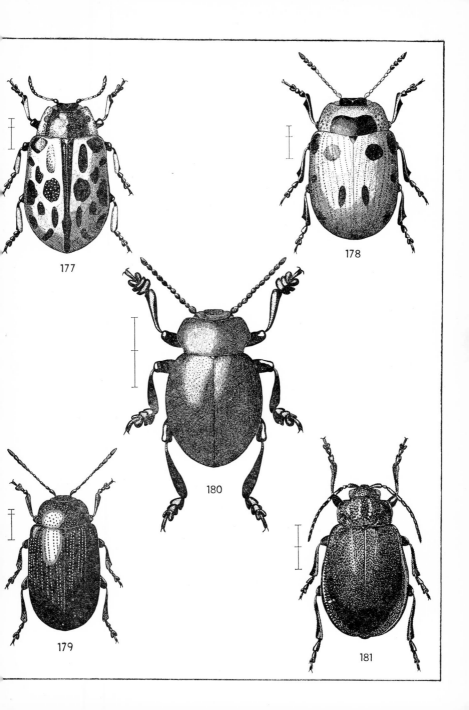

177

178

180

179

181

(*Mentha* species). *C. nobilis* L. ± 5 mm. Each el. with a longitudinal golden or silver metallic band, which vanishes when the insect dies.

— Upperside bearing spines.

Hispa (=*Hispella*) *atra* L. Fig. 185, p. 133. 3–4 mm. Black. On dry pastures.

RHYNCHOPHORA

1. Rostrum very short and broad, ant. not distinctly elbowed.   2
— Rostrum always well developed.

CURCULIONIDAE (Weevils) 3

There are about 1000 European species, of which over 600 occur in the British Isles.

2. Ant. with enlarged apical segs. but without a distinct club.   ANTHRIBIDAE

Brachytarsus nebulosus Forst. Fig. 191, p. 137. 2–4 mm. Black, el. with grey or yellow scaly patches. On pine bark. *Anthribus albinus* L. Fig. 192, p. 137. 7–10 mm. Black, clothed with brown scales, with a pattern of white hairs. In deciduous woods.

— Ant. with distinct compact club, body cylindrical.

IPIDAE (Bark Beetles)

The larvae, which bore galleries of a characteristic pattern in the wood immediately beneath the bark, cause serious damage, particularly in coniferous forests. There are about 100 European species, of which about 60 occur in the British Isles.
Scolytus scolytus F. (Large Elm Bark Beetle). Fig. 186, p. 135. 4–5·5 mm. Black, legs and el. red. Chiefly in elm.

Figs. 182–5: 182 *Agelastica alni* L., p. 130; 183 *Phyllotreta undulata* Kutsch. (Small Striped Flea Beetle), p. 130; 184 *Altica oleracea* L., p. 130; 185 *Hispa atra* L., p. 132.

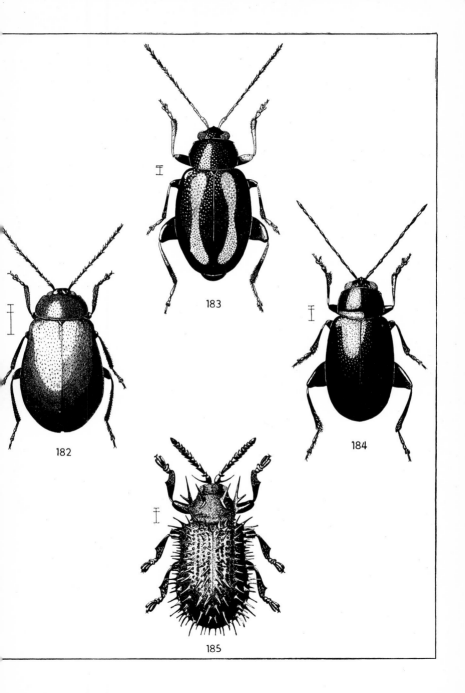

183

182

184

185

Blastophagus piniperda L. (Pine-Shoot Beetle). Fig. 187, p. 135. 3·5–4·5 mm. Black, el. rarely red. Mainly in pines, but also in other coniferous trees. *Polygraphus polygraphus* L. Fig. 188, p. 135. 2·2–3 mm. Brown. In spruce and pine. *Ips typographus* L. Fig. 189, p. 135. 4·2–5·5 mm. El. often brown. In spruce and pine; rare in the British Isles.

CURCULIONIDAE (Weevils)

3. Rostrum short and stout, flattened above, not cylindrical.   4
— Rostrum long, or if short then cylindrical.   5
4. Claws free.

> *Otiorrhynchus niger* F. Fig. 193, p. 137. 6·5–12 mm. Black, legs red, el. clothed with sparse grey pubescence. In coniferous woods. *O. ligustici* L. 9–12 mm. Black, upperside clothed with a dense, variegated grey pubescence. In dry places. *O. singularis* L. (Clay-coloured Weevil). 6·5–8 mm. Black, clothed with brown and yellow-brown scales. This species is sometimes a garden pest; the larvae attack raspberries and hops.

— Claws fused at the base.

> *Phyllobius calcaratus* F. (Leaf Weevil). Colour Plate VI, fac. p. 42. 8–12 mm. Black, legs usually lighter; upperside usually clothed with metallic green scales. Chiefly on alders. *P. pyri* L. (Common Leaf Weevil, Large Green Weevil). 5–6·5 mm. Similar to the preceding species, but smaller. On deciduous trees. *Sitona lineatus* L. (Pea and Bean Weevil). Fig. 194, p. 137. 4–5 mm. Upperside clothed with scales forming indistinct light and dark lines. A pea and bean pest.

5. Ant. elbowed.   6

Figs. 186–9: 186 *Scolytus scolytus* F. (Large Elm Bark Beetle), p. 132; 187 *Blastophagus piniperda* L. (Pine-Shoot Beetle), p. 134; 188 *Polygraphus polygraphus* L., p. 134; 189 *Ips typographus* L., p. 134.

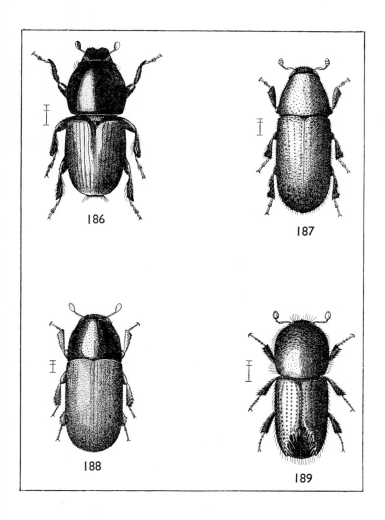

186

187

188

189

— Ant. not elbowed.
6. Large species, body elongate, ± cylindrical.

> *Bothynoderes punctiventris* Germ. Fig. 195, p. 137. 10–14 mm. Black, clothed with grey scales. Underside with numerous black spots. A pest in beet fields. *Lixus paraplecticus* L. Fig. 196, p. 139. 13–24 mm. Black, clothed with fine grey pubescence. Fresh specimens are sprinkled with an orange or yellow powder. On plants in marshy places.

— Body broader, or if narrow then small.   7
7. Base of ant. visible from above.   8
— Base of ant. not visible from above (ant. inserted near the underside of the rostrum). *Pissodes* belongs here, but is included under 8, because of its external resemblance to *Hylobius*.   9
8. Body less than 8 mm. long.

> *Phytonomus arator* L. Fig. 197, p. 139. 5–7 mm. Dark-coloured, upperside with lighter (grey and brown) longitudinal markings. In meadows. *Alophus triguttatus* F. 6–8 mm. Black, clothed with brown scales, upperside with patchy white markings, el. with 3 large white patches. In meadows.

— Body more than 10 mm. long.

> 1. Shoulders angular: *Lepyrus capucinus* Schall. 10–12 mm. Brown or grey, pnt. and el. patches (especially 2 more distinct patches behind the middle) light brown to whitish. In meadows. *Hylobius piceus* Deg. Fig. 198, p. 139. 12–16 mm. Black or brown, upperside with many small yellow pubescent patches. *H. abietis* L. (Pine Weevil). Fig. 199, p. 135. 10–13 mm. Similar to the

Figs. 190–5: 190 *Bruchus pisorum* L. (Pea Beetle), p. 116; 191 *Brachytarsus nebulosus* Forst., p. 132; 192 *Anthribus albinus* L., p. 132; 193 *Otiorrhynchus niger* F., p. 134; 194 *Sitona lineatus* L. (Pea and Bean Weevil), p. 134; 195 *Bothynoderes punctiventris* Germ., p. 136.

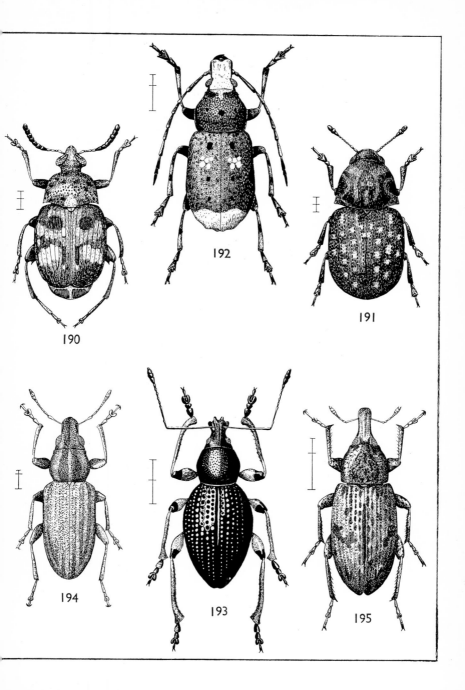

190

192

191

194

193

195

preceding species, but el. patches forming indistinct transverse rows. On pines and firs. *Pissodes pini* L. (Banded Pine Weevil). 8–10 mm. Similar to the preceding species but smaller. On pines and firs.

2. Shoulders rounded: *Liparus germanus* L. Fig. 200, p. 139. 13–16 mm. Black, el. with patches of yellow-grey pubescence. *L. coronatus* Goeze. 12–15 mm. El. almost glabrous with a few yellowish hairs. Both species live under moss and stones.

9. Body elongate or oval.

Baris chlorizans Germ. 3·5–6 mm. Metallic blue-black, fairly shining. Similar in shape to *Calandra granaria*. On Cruciferae (Shepherd's purse and its allies). *Calandra granaria* L. (Grain Weevil). Fig. 202, p. 141. ± 3 mm. Brown, upperside shining; pnt. with large elongate punctures. *C. oryzae* L. (Rice Weevil). Similar to the preceding species but with the upperside matt; pnt. more thickly and finely punctured. Both species are pests of stored grain, and the latter also of rice. *Dorytomus longimanus* Forst. Fig. 203, p. 141. 4·5–8 mm. Reddish-brown; front femora toothed. On willows (*Salix* species).

— Body ± spherical or very shortly oval.

1. Body relatively large, rostrum conspicuously long. *Curculio nucum* L. (Nut Weevil). Colour Plate VI, fac. p. 42. 6–9 mm. The larvae are found in hazel-nuts.

2. Body smaller, hind femora not thickened. *Ceuthorrhynchus* Germ. Side pieces of mesothorax visible from above (at the sides, between the pthx. and el.). Numerous monophagous species. *C. geographicus* Goeze. Fig. 201, p. 139. 4–5 mm. Black, with whitish markings. On Viper's bugloss (*Echium*). *Cionus scrophulariae* L. (Figwort Weevil). Colour Plate VI, fac. p. 42. 4–5 mm. Side pieces

Figs. 196–201: 196 *Lixus paraplecticus* L., p. 136; 197 *Phytonomus arator* L., p. 136; 198 *Hylobius piceus* Deg., p. 136; 199 *Hylobius abietis* L. (Pine Weevil), p. 136; 200 *Liparus germanus* L., p. 138; 201 *Ceuthorrhynchus geographicus* Goeze, p. 138.

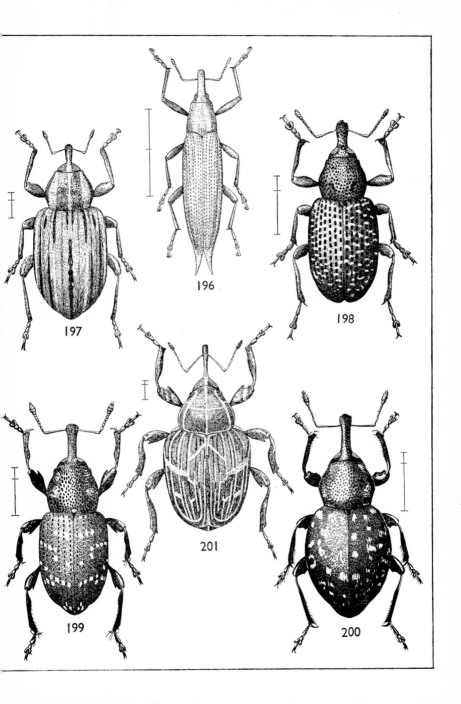

of mesothorax not visible from above; markings distinct. On Figwort (*Scrophularia*).

3. Body small, hind coxae thickened (jumping Beetles). *Rhynchaenus salicis* L. Colour Plate VI, fac. p. 42. 2–2·5 mm. On willows (*Salix* species).

10. Rostrum slender, or at most slightly expanded towards the tip. El. oval.

> *Apion apricans* Hbst. (Clover Seed Weevil). Fig. 204, p. 141. 3–3·5 mm. Dark metallic blue, legs and ant. base red. In clover fields. *A. sanguineum* Deg. 2·5–3·5 mm. Similar to the preceding species but dull red in colour.

— Rostrum stouter, distinctly expanded towards the tip. El. triangular.

> *Deporaus betulae* L. Fig. 205, p. 141. 2·5–4 mm. Unicolorous black. Hind femora of ♂ thickened. On birches. *Rhynchites auratus* Scop. Fig. 206, p. 141. 5·5–9 mm. Golden-green to purple, pubescent; ♂ with spine on either side of the pthx. On vines and fruit trees. *Byctiscus populi* L. (Poplar Leaf Roller). Colour Plate VI, fac. p. 42. 4·5–6 mm. Similar to the preceding species; upperside glabrous. On poplars. *Attelabus nitens* Scop. Colour Plate VI, fac. p. 42. 4–6 mm. Black, pnt. and el. red; el. finely punctate-striate. On young oaks. *Apoderus coryli* L. Fig. 207, p. 141. 4–6 mm. Similar to the preceding species. Black, pnt. el. and legs partly red; el. coarsely punctate-striate. On hazel-nut bushes.

Figs. 202–7: 202 *Calandra granaria* L. (Grain Weevil), p. 138; 203 *Dorytomus longimanus* Forst., p. 138; 204 *Apion apricans* Hbst. (Clover Seed Weevil), p. 140; 205 *Deporaus betulae* L., p. 140; 206 *Rhynchites auratus* Scop., p. 140; 207 *Apoderus coryli* L., p. 140.

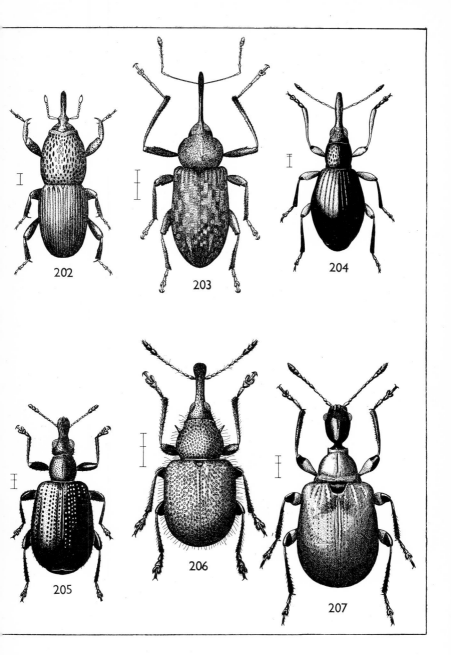

202

203

204

205

206

207

Appendix

KEYS TO THE SUPERFAMILIES
OF THE POLYPHAGA

From Crowson, The Classification of the Families
of the British Coleoptera, published in parts in
The Entomologist's Monthly Magazine, 1949–53.

1. Abdomen with distinct pleural sclerites (chitinous plates lying at the side between the tergite and sternite) of the 2nd abdominal segment.
   POLYPHAGA-HAPLOGASTRA   2

— Abdomen with the pleurite of the 2nd sternite fused to that of the 3rd.   *POLYPHAGA-SYMPHIOGASTRA*   5

2. Antennae with apical segments enlarged on one side to form a lamellate club, or with the terminal segment enlarged on one side.   *SCARABAEOIDEA*

   (LUCANIDAE, TROGIDAE, GEOTRUPIDAE, SCARABAEIDAE.)

— Antennae, if clubbed, never with apical segments forming a lamellate club.   3

3. Antennae shorter than the palpi.
   HYDROPHILOIDEA

   (HYDRAENIDAE, HYDROCHIDAE, SPERCHEIDAE, HYDRO-PHILIDAE, GEORYSSIDAE.)

— Antennae longer than the palpi.   4

4. Antennae not elbowed, rarely with a club.
   STAPHYLINOIDEA

   (Sphaeriidae, Clambidae, Ptiliidae, Leptinidae, Anisotomidae, Silphidae, Scaphidiidae, Scydmaenidae, Staphylinidae, Pselaphidae.)

— Antennae elbowed, with a compact 3-segmented club.
   HISTEROIDEA

   (Sphaeritidae, Histeridae.)

5. Legs always without trochanters; ♀ without wings or elytra.   *STYLOPOIDEA*

   Up to the present time, this family has been treated as an independent order (STREPSIPTERA). The insects are parasitic on bees, occupying the space between the body wall of the abdomen and the internal organs. The ♂♂ have milky-white wings.

— Legs always with distinct trochanters.   6
6. Posterior edges of hind coxae produced into flat plates (femoral plates), so that the retracted femora are at least partially covered.   *DASCILLIFORMIA* 7
— Posterior edges of hind coxae without femoral plates, or if femoral plates are present, then the antennae with the 3 apical segments very long or forming a club.
   CUCUJIFORMIA 12
7. Middle coxae widely separated, hind coxae close together.   *BYRRHOIDEA*

   (Byrrhidae.)

— If the middle coxae are widely separated, then the hind coxae also widely separated.   8
8. Hind femora completely covered by the femoral plates of the coxae; front coxae projecting.   *DASCILLOIDEA*

   (Dascillidae, Helodidae, *Eucinetidae.)

— If the front coxae are projecting, the femoral plates of the hind coxae are usually incomplete, so that the

143

retracted femora are not entirely covered. The femoral plates are well developed in the *RHIPICEROIDEA*. This family is not represented in Europe. 9

9. Fronto-clypeal suture (dividing the clypeus from the frons or forehead) distinct. *DRYOPOIDEA*

(HETEROCERIDAE, LIMNICHIIDAE, DRYOPIDAE, ELMIDAE.)

— Fronto-clypeal suture not distinct. 10

10. Abdomen with first 2 visible sternites fused together and the suture between them partially obliterated. *BUPRESTOIDEA*

(BUPRESTIDAE).

— Suture between abdominal sternites 1 and 2 as well marked as between the following sternites. 11

11. Prosternal intercoxal process produced into a spine; hind coxae with distinct and complete femoral plates. *ELATEROIDEA*

(ELATERIDAE, TRIXAGIDAE, *CEROPHYTIDAE, EUCNEMIDAE.)

— Prosternal intercoxal process short; hind coxae with femoral plates very narrow. *CANTHAROIDEA*

(DRILIDAE, *HOMALISIDAE, LAMPYRIDAE, CANTHARIDAE.)

12. Hind coxae with femoral plates; Tarsi 5-, 5-, 5-segmented. 13

— Hind coxae without femoral plates. 14

13. Prothorax usually transverse (i.e. broader than long) or flattened, not hood-like. *DERMESTOIDEA*

(*DERODONTIDAE, *NOSODENDRIDAE, DERMESTIDAE, *THORICTIDAE; this last family has been introduced to Central Europe.)

— Prothorax more or less globular, produced forward over the head in a hood-like fashion. *BOSTRYCHOIDEA*

(ANOBIIDAE, PTINIDAE, BOSTRICHIDAE, LYCTIDAE.)

144

14. Tarsi all 4-segmented.   17
 — Tarsi variously constructed, or if all 4-segmented then the head without a rostrum.   15

15. Tarsi all 5-segmented; front coxae projecting.   16
 — Front coxae rounded, or if projecting then tarsi 5-, 5-, 4-segmented.   *CUCUJOIDEA*

    I. *CLAVICORNIA*: Nitidulidae, Rhizophagidae, Sphinidae, Passandridae (sometimes introduced into Britain in grain cargoes from the tropics), Cucujidae, Silavanidae, Cryptophagidae, Byturidae, Erotylidae, Phalacridae, Ciidae, Cerylonidae, Corylophidae, Coccinellidae, Endomychidae, *Merophysiidae, Lathridiidae.

    II. *HETEROMERA*: Mycetophagidae, Colydiidae, Lagriidae, Tenebrionidae, Alleculidae, Salpingidae, Pythidae, Pyrochroidae, Melandryidae, Scraptidae, Mordellidae, Rhipiphoridae, Meloidae, Oedemeridae, Anthicidae.

16. 5 or 6 abdominal segments visible.

                                           CLEROIDEA

    (Trogositidae = Ostomidae, Cleridae, Melyridae, Phloeophilidae, this last family includes only a single species, *Phloeophilus edwardsi* Steph.)

 — 7 abdominal sternites visible.

                                     LYMEXYLOIDEA

    (Lymexylidae.)

17. Head short, without a rostrum.

                                   CHRYSOMELOIDEA

    (Cerambycidae, Chrysomelidae, Bruchidae.)

 — Head with a rostrum, which may, however, be very short.   *CURCULIONOIDEA*

    (Anthribidae, Nemonychidae, Attelabidae, Apionidae, Curculionidae.)

GLOSSARY

For the names of the different parts of the body, see Figures on pages 13 and 52.

The following technical terms are used in the keys.

Apex. Tip, top.

Apical. At the tip; the part of the organ farthest from the body.

Basal. At the base; the part of the organ nearer the body.

Base. The bottom.

Clavate. Clubbed or club-shaped.

Decumbent. Lying down.

Depressed. Flattened as if by pressure from above.

Disk. The central portion.

Emarginate. With a piece cut out of the margin, notched.

Explanate. Widened out, expanded.

Filiform. Thread-like; elongate and of about the same thickness throughout.

Glabrous. Smooth, without hairs or scales.

Geniculate. Elbowed or kneed.

Humeral. Relating to the shoulder.

Humerus. Shoulder.

Impunctate. Without punctures.

Interval. The space between elytral striae or punctures of the pronotum.

Keel. A fine raised line.

Lamellate. Plated.

Lateral. At the side.

Margin. The outer edge.

Margined. Furnished with a more or less distinctly pronounced outer edge.

Median.	Situated in the middle.
Membranous.	Thin and transparent.
Moniliform.	Like a string of beads.
Pectinate.	Toothed like a comb.
Penultimate.	The last but one.
Pore.	Large isolated puncture.
Pubescent.	Furnished with hair.
Punctate.	Furnished with punctures.
Puncture.	A small depression on the surface, generally round.
Quadrate.	Square.
Rugose.	Wrinkled.
Sculpture.	Modification of the surface in the way of punctuation, striae, elevations, etc.
Serrate.	With teeth like a saw.
Setae.	Long or short outstanding bristles or stiff hairs.
Sinuate.	When a margin is slightly curved.
Striae.	Impressed lines.
Striate.	Furnished with striae.
Squamae.	Scales.
Squamose.	Covered with larger or smaller squamae or scales.
Suture.	Line on which the elytra join; point of junction between any two parts.
Terminal.	The last, the end of a series.
Transverse.	Broader than long.
Truncate.	Abruptly cut across in a straight line.
Tubercle.	A small abrupt elevation of varying form.
Unicolorous.	Of the same colour throughout.

ABBREVIATIONS

The following abbreviations of authors' names have been employed in the text. All other names have been given in full.

Bl.	Block	*Küst.*	Küster
Bon.	Bonelli	*Kutsch.*	Kutschera
Cederh.	Cederhjelm	*L.*	Linnaeus
Charp.	Charpentier	*Laich.*	Laicharting
Chaud.	Chaudoir	*Latr.*	Latreille
Com.	Comolli	*Marsh.*	Marsham
Deg.	Degeer	*Müll.*	Müller
Dej.	Dejean	*Obenb.*	Obenberger
Donov.	Donovan	*Oliv.*	Olivier
Duft.	Duftschmid	*Pall.*	Pallas
Dum.	Dumeril	*Panz.*	Panzer
Eschsch.	Eschscholtz	*Payk.*	Paykull
F.	Fabricius	*Pill. et*	Piller and
Fald.	Faldermann	*Mitt.*	Mitterpacher
Fall.	Fallén	*Pontopp.*	Pontoppidan
Forst.	Forster	*Preyssl.*	Preyssler
Fröl.	Frölich	*Quens.*	Quensel
Fuessl.	Fuessly	*Sam.*	Samouelle
Geoffr.	Geoffroy	*Schall.*	Schaller
Germ.	Germar	*Schr.*	Schrank
Grav.	Gravenhorst	*Schreib.*	Schreiber
Gyllh.	Gyllenhal	*Scop.*	Scopoli
Hbst.	Herbst	*Serv.*	Serville
Hochw.	Hochenwarth	*Shp.*	Sharp
Hoffm.	Hoffmann	*Steph.*	Stephens
Illig.	Illiger	*Suff.*	Suffrain
Kiesw.	Kiesenwetter	*Thunb.*	Thunberg
Kugel.	Kugelann		

BIBLIOGRAPHY

Balfour-Browne, F., *British Water Beetles*. 2 volumes. Ray Society, 1940 and 1950.

Crowson, R., *The Classification of the British Coleoptera*. Published in parts in *The Entomologist's Monthly Magazine*, 1949–53. This work is to be published in book form.

Dibb, J. R., *Field Book of Beetles*. Brown, 1948.

Fowler, W. E., *Coleoptera of the British Isles*. 5 volumes. L. Reeve, 1887–91 (out of print).

Joy, N. H., *A Practical Handbook of British Beetles*. Witherby, 1932 (out of print).

Kloet, G. S. and Hinks, W. D., *A Check List of British Insects*. 1945.

Van Emden, F. I., *Larvae of British Beetles*. Published in parts in *The Entomologist's Monthly Magazine*, **75**: 257–73; **76**: 7–13; **77**: 117–27, 181–92; **78**: 253–72; **79**: 209–23, 259–70; **81**: 13–37; **83**: 154–71; **85**: 265–83.

The Royal Entomological Society is publishing, in parts, a series of Handbooks for the Identification of British Insects. So far the following have appeared:

 Hydradephaga, by F. Balfour-Browne.
 Coccinellidae and Sphindidae, by R. D. Pope.
 Lagriidae to Meloidae, by F. D. Buck.
 Cerambycidae, by E. A. J. Duffy.
 Scolytidae and Platypodidae, by E. A. J. Duffy.

(The parts are obtainable at the Society's Rooms, 41 Queen's Gate, London, S.W.7.)

The following works in French and German are also very useful:

Calwer, G. C., *Käferbuch*. 6th edition. Stuttgart, 1916.

Ganglbauer, L., *Die Käfer Mittleuropas*. 4 volumes. Vienna, 1892–1904.

Horion, A., *Nachtrag zu Reitters Fauna Germanica*. Krefeld, 1933. *Verzeichnis der Käfer Mittleuropas*. 2 volumes. Stuttgart, 1951–2.

Kuhnt, P., *Illustrierte Bestimmungs-Tabellen der Käfer Deutschlands*. Stuttgart, 1913.

Reitter, E., *Fauna Germanica*. Die Käfer des Deutschen Reiches. 5 volumes. Stuttgart, 1908–16.

Bestimmungstabellen der europäischen Coleopteren, No. 1–115, 118–23. Vienna and Troppau, 1879–1942.

Bestimmungstabellen der europäischen Käfer in: *Koleopterologische Rundschau, Vienna*, 1939–51.

Faune de France, Coléoptères. Paris. A series of works by specialists (in progress).

INDEX OF SCIENTIFIC NAMES

Numbers in heavy type refer to illustrations

153

INDEX OF COMMON NAMES

Numbers in heavy type refer to illustrations

157